THE OWL ON THE TEAPOT

THE OWL
ON THE TEAPOT

JOAN GRANT

With a Foreword by Katie Boyle

WHITTET BOOKS

Frontispiece: Wol

First published 1991
© 1991 by Joan Grant

Whittet Books Ltd, 18 Anley Road, London W14 0BY
All rights reserved
Design by Paul Saunders

British Library Cataloguing in Publication Data
Grant, Joan
 The owl on the teapot.
 1. Great Britain. Bird sanctuaries
 I. Title
 082639.9782941

 ISBN 0-905483-87-1

Typeset by Litho Link Ltd, Welshpool, Powys, Wales.
Printed and bound by Billings of Worcester.

CONTENTS

Foreword by KATIE BOYLE

THIS is the most enchanting book. I have laughed, cried and learnt so much from Joan Grant's stories.

Oh, how I wish I'd known her when I picked up a tiny fledgling from being stalked by a cat on the shores of Lake Léman, in (Lausanne) in Switzerland.

I called him Humperdinck, weaned him on chopped worms (till I discovered mince beef was acceptable) and mashed cherries and peaches for 'afters'!

As a barely feathered scrap I brought him back to England in a Swiss chocolate box, with airholes strategically placed to avoid draughts, and he was never to know the confines of a cage – his Mobile Home was a hay and tissue-lined raffia basket, and his constant companion, a tiny Sleeve Peke. They became great telly addicts, with Humperdinck silent and snuggled into Mitzi's furry frontage, until she dared to move and interrupt his viewing.

He had a very active and happy life with me, but I doubt whether he ever knew he belonged to the bird kingdom, and I've always feared I did the wrong thing when, after eight months, I left this precious little dunnock in a bird sanctuary. Admittedly, it was in a large aviary populated only by the smallest of birds, but I had spent so many hours persuading this petrified little creature, always in vain, that he was feathered rather than furry, and I hadn't dared release him from a seventh floor London flat window, or let him fly on to a tree in a London park.

So was I guilty, through ignorance, of cruelty? Luckily, Mrs Grant assures me that I wasn't.

I shall certainly go and seek her advice when a lady Cockateel called Henry, with a daily habit of sailing in a small tub on his owner's bath water, comes to spend his holiday fortnight with me and my four rescued dogs.

The Owl on the Tea-pot was compulsive reading for me – Joan Grant's style is swift and full of humour, and I became as fascinated by her and her long-suffering Eric, as I did by the behaviour of her many and varied visitors. I felt positively bereft when I came to the last page of these real-life comedies and dramas. I think a lot of people will get enormous pleasure from this book.

= 1 =

LOOKING BACK

'No, Stikki ... that hurts!' I protested, reaching up to remove the kestrel from his favourite perch on my head. 'Besides, you're quite heavy.'

It wasn't easy, typing with a bird of prey clinging to your scalp. Normally very gentle – I never had to wear gloves when handling him – his talons were like needles as he gripped my head to keep his balance.

'Stikki! Go and perch somewhere else!'

Was acupuncture like this?

The kestrel flew away across the room, deliberately almost brushing the soft feathery head of my tawny owl, Wol, who was watching blinkily from *his* favourite perch on the teapot. Wol turned his head slowly and stared at Stikki disdainfully, blinking his disapproval of such flippancy. Brought up with him and the best of friends, Stikki often teased his more staid companion in this way. Wol didn't really come to life until much later in the evening.

I sighed, leaning back in my chair. To my left three young starlings in a box squawked loudly for their umpteenth meal of the day, their enormous yellow beaks gaping. On the other side of me the inmates of a stack of large wooden cages fidgeted, waiting to be covered for the night: young blackbirds, a song-thrush, two pigeons, a collared dove and a robin. Four little sparrows in the cage under the window were silent; sparrows go to bed very early and I'd covered them some time ago.

A glance at the clock told me it was time for Harold's supper – I'd better go and defrost his sardines. Harold was a young heron with a king-sized appetite. I closed my eyes momentarily, thinking back to how it all began. How had my small furnished bed-sitter become a busy bird hospital with people bringing me around a hundred and fifty wild bird patients a year?

1

'A hundred and fifty birds!' my elderly mother once exclaimed over the telephone. 'What . . . all at once?'

The mind boggled. 'No, dear . . . during the course of the year,' I explained patiently.

'Oh, I see,' she said, after a pause, sounding as if she didn't.

As a young woman I'd had a somewhat chequered career. After leaving school I was sent away to learn all about horses, and eventually became a riding instructress. But war had broken out and as soon as I was eighteen I joined the WAAF and became first a radar operator and then a mechanic. After the war and now used to tinkering with transmitters and things, I got a job as assistant to a radio engineer and spent each day repairing people's radios and scrambling about on rooftops with my boss fixing television aerials. I shudder to think of it now, feeling nervous and giddy if more than five feet from the ground.

My mother was ill and I had to go home for a spell; afterwards, disenchanted with the dusty insides of radios, I decided I wanted to go abroad. I put an ad. in a European newspaper saying I was prepared to 'do anything anywhere'.

'I don't think you should have worded it quite like that, dear,' remarked my mother, frowning over her steamed plaice. 'You might get some . . . well, rather strange replies.'

She was quite right, of course: I did. I clearly remember giggling over one reply from a French farmer which, when translated, suggested he was 'very experienced in life and love' and needed an assistant. However, among other dubious replies there was one offering me a post as governess to two little French girls in Switzerland and this I accepted. My mother was somewhat relieved. It sounded respectable enough, though she was worried about what might happen to me on the long train journey.

'I'm not travelling on the Orient Express, you know . . . of course I'll be all right.'

A year later I returned; I'd had enough of children and had now decided I wanted to go to sea. In went another ad., and I ended up as a sort of deck-hand and chief-cook-and-bottle-washer on a 250-ton steam yacht anchored in the middle of Southampton Water. My mother feared the worst; I can see now I should never have told her that when the yacht was done up we were going to trade to and from the West African coast – at least, this was the general idea. Now she was convinced that her daughter was in the clutches of some white slave trader.

She needn't have worried; just about everything went wrong and we

2

never went anywhere. I left after a few weeks.

After a lean and jobless spell I tried my hand as a door-to-door saleswoman, carting an enormous fluffy wool blanket around in a suitcase; by bus, as I had no car in those days. After four hours I returned to base, disillusioned, and collected my cards. I'd realized after the first door slammed in my face that the whole thing was a ghastly mistake. So I got a job in the book department of a large store.

Selling books was a whole lot easier than selling blankets but there wasn't enough action for my restless spirit, so after some months I left to take a position as general assistant in a 14th-century country hotel in East Sussex. I was very happy there – lots of running about – but a year later the place was sold and the new owners were bringing in their own staff, we were told.

I still hankered for a life on the ocean wave – was it something to do with being born under Pisces? – so I applied to every shipping line I'd ever heard of for a job as a stewardess. I was politely turned down by each and every one as I had no nursing experience – essential in those days – so I wrote to the airlines; at least I'd be travelling places, though I wasn't all that keen on flying, preferring the sea. Many interviews later I was accepted, and flew as an air stewardess with British European Airways, as it was then, for eleven years. The job was interesting but exhausting and far from the 'glamour' job most people thought; clutching my redundancy pay, I settled down afterwards for a well earned rest, feeling tired, a bundle of nerves and about ninety. I also bought a brand new car to replace my ancient Morris that had toadstools growing up through the floor at the back.

I was living in a furnished bed-sitter on the second floor of an old Victorian house; my small room, under sloping eaves, faced north across the large garden at the back of the house and had a lovely view of the fields all around, the front of the house bordering a busy main road.

It was here while I was recuperating after eleven years of living in suitcases that I reared my first bird . . .

=2=

KWEEKIE
THE SONG-THRUSH

THE bird was a song-thrush and I called him Kweekie. I don't think there'll ever be another Kweekie; certainly I've never come across another thrush remotely like him, though I've since reared many. From a small fledgling rescued from under the very nose of a prowling tabby cat he grew into a fine, adult bird, and the months he was with me were full of interest; for us both, I'm sure, for he had an insatiable curiosity and a great sense of humour, very obviously enjoying his rather strange life in the unnatural surroundings of my small bed-sitter to the full.

The young thrush was completely unafraid, tame as a dog and very affectionate. He got up to more tricks than a cartload of monkeys, and there was never a dull moment with Kweekie around. My room often resembled a cross between a children's playground and a battlefield, as he had the freedom of the room and was never caged. All I did was pin a net curtain across any open window.

Kweekie insisted on being fed every twenty minutes to begin with, starting at 4.30 a.m. sharp. He became positively demented if kept waiting any longer. I estimated I fed him some fifty meals a day, as a small fledgling, as he demanded food right up to 9.30 p.m., getting terribly upset if I tried to settle him for the night before this time. He grew fast, soon fluttering and jumping around the room and exploring every inch. All that food seemed to give him a terrific amount of energy!

He took to roosting at night in all sorts of peculiar places: like on the shade of my central ceiling light, the top of the wardrobe and even on the hook on my door. This latter place had clothes hanging on it and I was always relieved when he found somewhere else to perch as they were difficult to cover with the newspaper normally placed strategically underneath a favourite roost.

A bad sleeper, I sometimes read a book in the night, and Kweekie would fly down from wherever he was and stand close to my pillow; wearing his most ferocious expression, head feathers erect, he'd then utter short, sharp squeaks of annoyance, scolding me until I closed the book and put out the light. Then he'd quietly return to his roosting-place. If I was late getting up in the morning, though, he was equally insistent, flying on to the bed and running up and down on my prostrate body in a great state of agitation and pique, tweeking my ear, hair or neck each time he approached the pillow end and all the time squeaking his disapproval of my sluggishness. In the end I'd throw back the bedclothes with an 'Oh, all *right,* then' and draw back the curtains. Whereupon he'd partake of a hearty breakfast of raw mince, bread-and-milk and other tit-bits.

Letter-writing was one of the many things that seemed to fascinate him. He would watch me from across the room then fly over and land, plonk! right on the sheet of paper in front of me. If I brushed him away – it does cramp one's style having a song-thrush standing an inch in front of one's pen – Kweekie returned immediately to the same spot. Sometimes he watched from my shoulder, head on one side, and on occasions he tried to 'catch' the words as I wrote them . . . or so it appeared. A deep thinker, I'm sure, I believe it puzzled him; one minute there was a blank sheet of paper and the next instant dark squiggles appeared. Once when, intent on finishing a letter and catching the post, I failed to respond to his squeaking for food, the young thrush perched on my shoulder and yelled in my ear so loudly and insistently that I gave up. 'Okay, where's the mince, then?'

'Spoiled rotten!' my friend Betty exclaimed one morning over coffee. 'Honestly, fancy letting a bird boss you around.'

I smiled. Betty would never understand. She just about knew a robin from a sparrow; she was more interested in clothes and cooking and thought I was slightly mad letting a pampered thrush rule the roost.

One day I decided it was high time Kweekie took an interest in proper thrush food. So I filled a large wooden box with fairly deep soil, stuck in a twiggy perch and a piece of turf and made him a little indoor garden, complete with a dish of water for bathing. I put it on my chest of drawers, on thick newspaper, then sat back and watched.

Kweekie had been keeping the usual watchful eye on what I was doing and he flew over to investigate almost immediately, pecking at the soil. Quietly I laid a small worm in front of him, thinking he'd gobble it up, and I was totally unprepared for what happened next: the young thrush eyed the worm, head on one side, then gave it a tentative peck; the worm wriggled, as worms do, and Kweekie sprang on to my shoulder with a cry of alarm, literally trembling. I tried again, dangling the worm temptingly in front of him, but he backed away, shaking his head in annoyance and disgust as the worm touched his beak. After half an hour of this I gave up and the worm got a reprieve.

Next I tried a small snail; thrushes love snails, the book said. Kweekie didn't. Presented with a choice of snails and a flat stone as an anvil he flew away, bored. Admittedly he gave the creature a small peck – just to please me, I'm sure – but when the snail withdrew into its shell he lost interest. And so it was every time. We were getting nowhere fast. I tried cutting up small worms and popping small pieces down his throat but Kweekie spat them out with such venom that they landed on the floor, and it was a long time before he'd open his beak again.

It was no good. My young thrush made it perfectly clear that he considered worms in any shape or form an exceedingly poor substitute for minced steak, and snails and slugs nasty, unsavoury objects and definitely unfit for thrush consumption. And that was that. But I continued to leave a few worms in the soil of his box just in case he changed his mind one day.

A few weeks later I was sorry I'd done this, however. A rather nervous lady I knew brought me a book and we were chatting for a few minutes perched on my divan bed. Suddenly a rather battered and nasty looking worm flew through the air landing almost in her lap. She gave a little scream, jumped up and was through the door and halfway down the stairs before you could say knife, muttering, 'Well, goodbye . . . I really must be going,' as she fled. I didn't see her again for quite some time.

Kweekie was always attracted to water and any splashing noise. He liked to perch near the wash-basin and watch all that was going on; on the shelf above, he could admire himself in the oval mirror. Once, I remember, I was washing my hair and, eyes screwed up tight, I reached out a hand for the cup of diluted shampoo by my side. Instead of the cup, however, my fingers closed on a warm, feathery body; Kweekie was perching on the rim of the cup.

A running bath also delighted him and sometimes I took the song-thrush across the landing to the bathroom with me. He enjoyed playing in there. There was an old dressing-table with three mirrors that fascinated him, and of course all those lovely splashy noises from me in the bath, though only once did he come over to the latter and perch on the edge, peering down into the water. That was when I lay right back full length and my head must have disappeared from view; I think Kweekie came over to see what had happened to me, and, satisfied that I hadn't drowned or disappeared down the plug-hole, he then returned to the dressing-table and all those other thrushes.

Once, when he was older, he caught a huge spider in the bathroom and strutted around with its black legs sticking out from his beak like a bristly moustache as I lay cowering and horrified in the bath. He loved spiders, apparently considering them a great delicacy. Moths, too, were very popular and he gave chase enthusiastically whenever spotting one, usually cornering it under a lamp in the evening. The only flying insects he wouldn't eat were wasps and bluebottles; these were on his black-list, along with worms and snails.

Kweekie, always very playful, invented games to amuse himself. One of these I called Bouncing the Newspaper; it consisted of flying across the room and deliberately alighting on top of the open newspaper that I was holding up reading. This caused it to collapse and always made me jump, engrossed in reading as I always was. Then he sprang from the collapsed paper on to my chest, remaining there for a few seconds before turning and quickly bouncing the paper again as he flew away. He would repeat this several times, evidently thinking it was a huge joke, a really mischievous look on his face all the while.

Another trick he had was to stand on the newspaper as I held it upright, folded in half. This meant that I was only able to read half the page until he chose to move, and if I pushed him away he returned immediately and pattered up and down on the fold. Eventually I would be forced to stop reading, and I had a sneaking idea that this was partly the thrush's intention; he never liked to be ignored. Like a spoiled child, I mused, thinking of Betty's comment, but the little thrush possessed such charm that I was his more than willing slave.

Kweekie loved pushing small ornaments off a bookshelf, and he discovered one day that the mantelpiece over the gas-fire held some interesting ones as well, including a collection of small glass, china and wooden animals and a Spanish doll; also, a tradescantia plant in a small pot. He caused great havoc amongst these things as he took to flying around the room and dropping them all over the place. Somehow he managed to carry the most unwieldy and heavy objects in his beak, one favourite being a largish china crab, weighing nearly an ounce. He was for ever sneaking off with this crab and all its six legs were broken many times; I was always searching for particles of green, shiny leg on the floor and under the furniture in order to mend it, only to have it seized yet again. The Spanish doll came in for a good deal of attention, too, with Kweekie tugging away at her red-and-white spotted dress until she fell over. He tried desperately hard to get her over the edge of the mantelpiece, but she was six inches tall and he could never quite manage it. Some of the small animal ornaments disappeared completely, never to be seen again. I think the reason for this was that my awful thrush dropped them into the wastepaper basket, on occasions, and they remained there, unnoticed, when it was emptied. As for the poor tradescantia, he pulled so many pieces off my once trailing plant that the very longest stem ended up about two inches long.

Pencils and rubbers vanished at an alarming rate from the box in which they were kept; many's the time when, busy scribbling or drawing, I reached for a rubber only to find it had been spirited away, and I'd be extremely lucky if my spare pencils and other things hadn't followed suit. He took a real delight in removing these objects. Things that were too heavy to fly with were usually dragged or pushed, but remove them he did . . . somehow. Long pencils were gripped in his beak by the pointed lead, so they hung downwards as he flew, whereas thin, bridge type pencils were held in the middle, kept in a horizontal position as he flew. Rubbers he loved because they bounced; once when I started to boil some milk on a gas-ring there was a dreadful smell of burning rubber; Kweekie had deposited a small rubber in the centre of the ring. It took ages to clean the nasty molten mess away and the ring smelled every time I lit it for several days.

Kweekie liked balls, too. Ping-pong balls were pushed round the carpet with his beak and tennis balls stood on and rolled with his feet, with much wing fluttering and squeaking. He had a whale of a time, too, with a box full of bits and pieces which I sometimes gave him to play with on the floor. It contained things like old buttons, sea-shells, beads, pins, brooches and so on. Anything that rolled was pushed round the carpet at great speed, shells were hammered on the box and other articles flown around with. After about half an hour he'd get bored, just like a child, and then he'd fly off . . . leaving me to clear up the mess.

Woe betide me if I ever left my handbag open; practically everything would be removed except really impossible things, like a heavy compact. I once caught him trying to extract a large envelope that had got caught up in something; feet braced, he was pulling and tugging, trying to get it free. Sometimes I found drawing-pins in the bag – he loved them and flew round holding them daintily by the point.

He took a great interest in bed-making, too, and he invariably perched on my shoulder or back to supervise this operation. Sometimes he flew down on to the bed and, once, having been hindered in this way, I got my own back by lightly throwing a sheet over him. Kweekie wasn't in the least perturbed and still walked about on the bed when I snatched it off, almost defying me to do it again. But on one occasion I really got angry with him. I'd just put a clean white bottom sheet on the bed when I was called away to speak to someone outside the door. Kweekie was taking a bath in his garden box across the room. When I returned a few minutes later I was horrified to see little muddy thrush footmarks leading straight up the centre of my new whiter-than-white sheet and also on the still folded top sheet draped over a chair – and on the clean pillow cases. Kweekie had left his bath in order to inspect my clean linen . . .

Another time he pinched a lump of dried curry mix out of a bowl and flew away with it. I was afraid it might be something terribly hot so I gave chase and he finally dropped it. Shopping baskets he simply loved and he fell upon mine and inspected every item before I'd even got my coat off.

As he grew older Kweekie became less tolerant of visitors though he was never afraid of them. Mind you, he never liked them. He obviously considered the bed-sitter his room; I was merely there to look after and entertain him, and he resented intruders. If friends stayed for any length of time he flew down to a near-by vantage point and gave them the old head-feathers-erect-fierce-expression treatment, squeaking in his scolding manner. One day he did this so pointedly, persistently snapping at some friends of mine with crisp, staccato squeaks, that my friend's husband, Geoff, remarked, 'Perhaps we've outstayed our welcome?'

We all laughed and I apologized for Kweekie's bad manners, but they left soon afterwards.

A boyfriend of mine, given the same treatment, was less amused . . .

One day I took Kweekie out in the car to have tea with an elderly friend living twelve miles away. She loved birds and was anxious to meet him. He sat fairly and squarely on the edge of the front passenger seat, refusing to travel in a box, and as usual was completely unperturbed by things like the noise of the engine and passing traffic.

On our arrival my thrush was the model of good behaviour, daintily accepting a piece of cake before flying across the room from my shoulder to explore some interesting brass implements in the grate.

'Well!' exclaimed my friend. 'It's really extraordinary, isn't it? He isn't even afraid of Deidre. Just look at him!'

Deidre was her very excitable poodle, barking and straining at the leash to get at the thrush, who was now inspecting a copper coal-scuttle.

'What an amazing bird he is!' she went on. 'You'd think he'd be frightened, in a strange house and with Deidre making all this noise? Deidre, be quiet!' She gave the poodle a small slap and tightened her hold, but Kweekie had found more interesting things to bother about and was now playing with a small piece of coal.

Back home, Kweekie decided it was time he explored the landing outside my room. It was large and square with doors leading off all round and a staircase leading down. There were large glass panels in the centre and a high domed glass roof, letting light through to the floors below. Various plants in pots were arranged around held in by wire grilles, and there was also a white cupboard outside my door on which I kept a stuffed alligator – a relic of my flying days. There were other items of old furniture out there, too, and the young thrush thought it a wonderful playground.

He took to going out on the landing to play whenever I left my door open for him, pecking around in the flower-pots, running up and down the alligator's scaly back, poking underneath the old furniture and having a great time generally. He seemed especially fond of the alligator and used to perch on its head, apparently whispering sweet nothings in its ear for quite long periods.

One morning I couldn't find Kweekie anywhere. I'd been busy in my room and had clean forgotten he was outside on the landing. Now he seemed to have disappeared and there was no answering 'tseek tseek' when I called. I was worried.

'Er, have you seen my thrush, Kweekie?' I asked someone cleaning the stairs.

'No, sorry,' she replied, looking up.

I got the same answer everywhere; where had he gone?

'Kwee . . . kie!' I yelled. 'Where are you?'

Peering over the banisters a few minutes later – could he have gone downstairs? – I saw the bathroom door open on the floor below and out came the elderly gentleman who had a room near by. He was carrying a towel over one arm and he walked slowly through the arched doorway and across the landing down there and out of my sight. Next minute I heard voices – then he reappeared and looked up at me.

'If you're looking for the bird I've put it out of the window,' he announced, immediately turning and disappearing again before I could say a word.

Running downstairs to the bathroom he'd just vacated I opened one of the sloping fanlight windows outwards and there was Kweekie on the sloping tiled roof to one side of it. He was crouching there motionless, looking very bewildered, and obviously hadn't attempted to move although I found out later that he must have been out there at least twenty minutes. Apparently the old gentleman thought he was a wild bird that had somehow managed to get into the house and he thought he was doing it a favour in putting it outside again. He must have been the only person in the house who hadn't heard of Kweekie.

Grabbing the thrush, I carried him back upstairs. I could see he was very put out; thoroughly upset about the whole thing. There he was inspecting the bathwater downstairs – he must have heard it running – when a huge hairy hand grabbed him and whoosh! he was out on the roof.

He flew up on to the wardrobe and sulked for quite some time. A few weeks later Kweekie started singing. It wasn't the usual sub-song of a captive bird but a loud, full-throated thrush song. He sang on and off all day, so loudly that he could be heard two floors below in the hall. For the first time the next day, he became restless and flew to the window, wanting to go.

He was a fine, adult song-thrush and I knew he was ready to face the outside world.

Opening the window I let him fly down into the garden. I went outside and saw him pecking around in some leaves; when I spoke to him he looked up and answered, but I could tell he didn't wish to come inside again.

I saw him several times after that and he seemed fine. I was a little worried about his dislike of worms and snails but presumed he'd soon get to like them when there was no raw mince forthcoming. My room seemed very empty afterwards for a long time. I missed him very much. Kweekie had been my constant companion for exactly five months.

3

A VERY SPECIAL SPARROW

AFTER Kweekie's departure and the return of law and order to my small room I took two part-time jobs; the first was secretary to the banqueting manager at a famous riverside hotel near here, and the other was a job as gardener two days a week. Regarding the former I couldn't do shorthand and I was a rotten typist but I had a very tolerant and charming boss and we muddled along. The gardening was very hard work indeed but I loved it.

In between all this I wrote a book about Kweekie.

In a way that song-thrush was instrumental in changing my life. Not only did he awaken a dormant interest I'd always had in birds but, through him, I met my future husband.

It happened in this way: unable to get my book published, I heard about a gentleman on the floor below whose son worked for a London firm of publishers. This son apparently visited his father most weekends, and it was arranged that I should meet him one Sunday; I was hoping he could pull a few badly needed strings on my behalf. Well, he couldn't and didn't but there were compensations; two months later we were married.

We couldn't afford our own home so we moved into a double-room across the landing from my room. But there were problems. My new husband snored loudly and devastatingly, and when I recovered from the nervous breakdown that followed some months later there was nothing for it but single rooms with a good thick wall between us, sad as it was. So we ended up in the two single bed-sitters on the ground floor – which is where I was sitting with Stikki on my head.

My room this time measured roughly thirteen feet six inches by ten feet, and again faced north, looking over the garden and fields. I had a second window facing east with a view of the side garden, and my husband Eric had a room facing the same way.

12

For a time I'd kept up my hotel and gardening jobs after marrying, but, forced to give them up through ill health, I decided to work at home now. I earned a little money writing scripts for teenage picture magazines, and managed to sell about two thirds of all the oil paintings I did, mostly at local art shows; I found I had something of a flair for this latter occupation, having tried my hand at it.

Middle-aged and married, all traces of wanderlust seemed to have vanished. I no longer had any desire to become airborne or go to sea but was more than happy to have both feet planted firmly on the ground. And for the first time I had the opportunity to indulge in things pertaining to my real love in life, namely everything to do with nature, animals, birds and the countryside.

I spent many happy hours in the fields at the back and side of the house, particularly in the twenty-two acre field – Green Belt land – that was accessible from the side of our garden. The top part of this field consisted of quite a steep incline leading to a narrow lane, beyond which was another sloping field; a large and imposing Tudor mansion visible from the bottom of the big field was at the top of the hill. From up there you could see for miles. I never tired of gazing at the line of trees stretching almost the length of the field – chestnuts, elms, giant plane trees, ash, pine, aspen, cedars, sycamore, Ilex oak and the magnificent tall giant sequoias or redwood trees. These trees were part of the woods bordering a large, ornamental lake.

The woods and lake were favourite haunts of mine. Pink and yellow water-lilies flowered in season on the lake, huge clumps of yellow iris, and several tiny islands. A narrow winding path led round the lake and beyond the woods the other side were pony fields with shady chestnut trees and buttercups in the summer. In the spring the woods were carpeted with primroses, bluebells, scillas and wild daffodils. It was here that I was to release many birds I'd reared and saved in the years to come.

One day I was at home cleaning our two little rooms when my husband came in clutching a small cardboard-box. He had left the publishers now and was a driver for the local garage down the road.

'What have you got there?' I asked, switching off the Hoover.

'A sparrow,' he answered, opening the flaps of the box. 'It nearly got run over. Can't seem to fly.'

'Let's have a look.'

I took the little bird from him. She was the smallest sparrow I'd ever seen – less than two inches from her head to the beginning of a tiny tail;

a diminutive scrap of grey feathers and fluff, dirty, dusty and dishevelled. One little wing was small and deformed, her legs and feet thin and weak, and her feathers frayed with gaps where some flight feathers seemed to be missing altogether. She reminded me of a small, battered shuttlecock.

I called her Chirpy, and popped her into the soft inner portion of an old dunnock's nest I'd found in the field in a box containing soft hay, covering it with a cloth. Then I fed the little bird some morsels of bread-and-milk which she gulped down eagerly, opening her beak for more.

She looked warm and cosy settled in the nest and I was quite unprepared for what followed. Suddenly the continuous chirping stopped and she tumbled over the edge of the nest, her small body twisting and contorted, eyes closed, beak open, and neck screwed right round. Twisting and turning, she seemed to be fighting for her very life, sometimes over on her back, sometimes upright, her small, inadequate wings fluttering violently all the time and a kind of strangled chirp sounding at intervals like a cry for help.

I watched, horrified and helpless, convinced the little bird was going to die. But Chirpy didn't die; this convulsion was only the first of many she was somehow to survive. They occurred every hour or so those first few days, gradually lessening in frequency but never in violence. She was very quiet afterwards, blinking in a dazed manner, but usually within about ten minutes she had fully recovered; looking at her bright little eyes and listening to the renewed chirping, it was almost as if nothing had happened. And so it was each time.

I learned to accept the convulsions; indeed, there was nothing I could do except try to be at hand to stop the contorted little body from harming itself. I talked to her soothingly while they were happening, trying to comfort her in her distress though she was probably unaware of my presence or even of what was taking place. But I tried to somehow will her to hang on and live through each ordeal, praying silently that she would.

Chirpy ate well, in between all this, and her tail grew longer; at least that seemed more normal. But it became increasingly obvious that she was always going to be very under-sized, and it was doubtful whether she would ever fly properly. Every day I gave her a powdered yeast tablet, sprinkling this on the bread-and-milk, which she really loved, and gradually her legs grew stronger, thanks to the Vitamin B content. Soon she was able to hop normally; at first, her legs had been too weak.

After about two weeks I installed her in an old budgie cage. Carefully adapting it with twiggy perches, I put dry soil and a small bed of hay on the floor and fixed a corner platform made of cardboard high up in one corner, enclosed at the side and with a soft cloth as a roof, forming a little hidey-hole, which the sparrow grew to love. She always had her dust baths up there, never on the floor, for some unknown reason.

Chirpy loved this cage right from the first and became very conservative about its contents, hating anything to be moved. A new perch or something placed in a different position really upset her and was eyed with great disapproval.

Before she had a dust bath the little sparrow always picked up a small piece of hay from the floor of the cage and carried it up to the platform. I could never imagine why she did this. She held the hay in her beak all the time she was dust bathing. Water baths she took in a small plastic flower-pot holder which she liked held outside in the open doorway of her cage. She flatly refused to have one anywhere else.

After a second moult in the autumn it became even more apparent that Chirpy's wings were never going to carry her far. She could get very little lift from the inadequate primaries, some of which were twisted the wrong way, and she never managed to fly upwards more than about a foot, though she could manage about ten feet horizontally. Each 'sortie' from the cage was always accompanied by a loud squeak as she launched herself into space; I felt it was her equivalent of 'Well, here I go . . . keep your fingers crossed!' for often she fell short of her intended destination.

I collected seeding grasses from the fields, tying them in bunches and poking them through the bars of her cage. Her favourite was couch-grass and she also liked weed-seed. Like Kweekie, she loved insects, too, as she grew older, especially spiders and squashed earwigs (I had to kill and squash the latter). Digestive biscuits, ginger-nuts dunked in tea, Sugar Puffs soaked in milk, cheese, jelly, honey, peas, lettuce, beans, milk chocolate, apple, cherries, roast beef (but not lamb or pork) and short, lawn grass all featured on her menu. The latter she preferred cut up very fine with scissors, or she'd ignore it. Sunflower-seed kernels – I had to open the seeds for her – were also very popular, but Chirpy's favourite food of all was bread-and-milk and plain canary seed.

The little sparrow had a terrific phobia about colour, especially the colour of people's clothes. If I or anyone else wore red, orange, yellow, pink or tan she became terrified. Blues and greens she didn't mind, while brown, grey and black were tolerated sometimes but not always, depending on the article. Navy blue was all right, too, but mauve and purple she abhorred.

'Why are you putting your raincoat on out here?' asked Eric one day. 'In this dark passage?' He'd just dashed in for something and found me apparently dressing in the corridor.

'Chirpy doesn't like this coat,' I answered, doing up the buttons and tucking in a maroon coloured scarf.

'Good Lord! Why not?'

'Well, you know she's funny about colours.'

'But it's fawn . . . surely she doesn't mind that?'

'She's got a thing about raincoats.'

'Well, honestly . . . *I* don't know. It's ridiculous the way you spoil that bird.' He went into his room for something, looking annoyed, and I picked up my red-striped nylon shopping-bag – hidden outside my door by the wardrobe out there (Chirpy was terrified of this) and went shopping.

Another day a friend of mine called. 'Coo-eee. Anyone in?' she said, peeping round the door.

'Come in, Kay,' I said, then, turning, I quickly added, 'No, don't!'

Chirpy was on top of her cage near the window – another favourite place – and my friend was wearing a scarlet trouser suit!

'Kay, I'm sorry, but do you think you could slip on this dressing-gown over your jacket?' I murmured apologetically, drawing her into Eric's room next door. 'Only Chirpy's frightened of red.'

'What? Oh, I forgot.' She gave a little laugh, 'Well, all right.' Then, 'I don't know . . . you and your Chirpy!'

She sat down and I made coffee. Chirpy, uneasy, made it clear she wished to be put back into her cage. She'd probably seen the bottom of two red trouser legs below the dressing-gown.

'You know,' said Kay. 'She'd soon get used to the colours that frighten her if you kept wearing them and persevered.'

'She wouldn't – honestly. I've tried, but she just goes berserk.'

It wasn't just a question of pandering to Chirpy's whims. Her convulsions had almost ceased now, but there was a very real danger that if the little bird became very upset or frightened they could start again. I was told she should be kept as calm as possible. Admittedly I could have covered the cage, but she hated being covered during the day.

The little sparrow had her favourite things; she loved the old green and navy tartan rug on my bed and, oddly enough, a red-patterned cushion. She liked to hop on the rug if I laid it on the lawn during the summer, and sunbathe or snooze on the cushion. Sometimes I had a rest on my bed in the afternoon and Chirpy always lay in my hand, sleeping quietly with my fingers curled gently over her back, close to my face on the red cushion. She'd stay there until I moved.

In September we went on holiday to friends in Devon. Chirpy came too, travelling quite happily in her cage on the back seat of the car, eating, dust bathing, hopping around and snoozing the miles away just as if she were still in the room at home. The rug and the red cushion came too.

My friend, Ivy, hadn't seen the little sparrow though she'd heard all about her in letters, of course. On our arrival she followed me into the spare room. 'Well, uncover the cage. I'm dying to see her!'

I looked at the bed. 'Well . . . er, I think we'd better wait until the morning, Ivy. A strange room and everything, and she must be very tired.'

'Oh, yes, of course. I'll see her tomorrow then.'

I was tired, too. Too tired to explain that Chirpy would be terrified of Ivy's yellow jumper, and the candy-pink bedspread. In the morning Ivy looked curiously at the transformation that had taken place in her guest room. But she didn't say anything. She was a very dear friend and used to my pets and the strange things that sometimes happened. But she must have wondered why the pretty pink bedspread was now covered with a shabby looking old tartan rug and there was a tatty old red cushion at the pillow end. Chirpy's cage was on the cushion.

Later I explained and Ivy laughed. 'Oh, I *see*,' she said. 'I did wonder.'

Morning and evening I let the sparrow out for a hop around but during the day she remained in her cage on my bed while we were on holiday. Ivy kept an eye on her, but Chirpy didn't like her to go too near.

'You'll notice I'm wearing a blue jumper and skirt,' smiled Ivy as we set off for the beach some nine miles away. 'Wouldn't want to upset Chirpy.'

We didn't dare let their basset hound go into the room. Nor the three cats.

Back home, my little sparrow settled down to the old routine. Now and then she tried her hand at singing, usually when some noise such as bacon sizzling inspired her. She emitted a series of ear-splitting squeaky noises, rising and falling, rather like the cross between a child practising the violin and a donkey braying. It wasn't much of a song but it was all she could manage. Pop music, the louder the better, also seemed to inspire her, and once when I'd left the radio on and gone out of the room I returned to find her apparently singing a duet with Tom Jones. 'Delilah' has never sounded the same since . . .

I was still busy doing some oil painting and not having an easel I lay my Daler board – I couldn't afford a canvas – flat on the bed and leaned forward from the armchair to paint, my paints, etc., on a board on top of the radiator at my side. All very unconventional! One day I left a seascape I was painting and went out of the room for a few minutes. I'd forgotten Chirpy was perching on top of her cage. When I returned I found I had a sparrow with little blue feet. She'd managed to flutter over to the bed and had hopped across the blue sky at the top of my picture. I had quite a job cleaning her tiny toes.

Chirpy loved warmth and if ever she was even slightly under the weather I filled a baby's small rubber hot-water bottle I had with warm water and put it in her cage. Quick as a flash she'd jump down on to it, fluff out her feathers and close her eyes. She liked it on cold winter days, too, and after she'd had a bath.

From when she first came the little sparrow always enjoyed being held in my hand, preferably the right one. I decided that this was because, being right-handed, it was used more and therefore warmer. I became adept at lighting the gas, striking matches and doing other jobs that normally required two hands, with my left hand only, Chirpy curled up in the warm right one. She really loved being held at any time of the day.

One summer when we were in the garden Chirpy left me and hopped across the lawn to where another sparrow was eating the breadcrumbs I'd thrown. The normal sparrow ignored her at first, but then, when Chirpy hopped closer, it turned and pecked my little bird before flying away. Chirpy went on standing there for a while and I wondered if she felt unhappy at this rejection. I felt sorry for her – she looked such a tiny scrap beside the other sparrow. Next minute, however, she hopped back to the rug and climbed on to the red cushion for a snooze in the sun, seeming totally unconcerned.

She was a dear little bird and I think Eric was almost as fond of her as I was.

Chirpy died very suddenly one October evening. The vet who came in answer to my frantic plea thought it was probably pneumonia, though he couldn't be sure. It was only an hour earlier that I'd noticed her laboured breathing and realized there was something wrong; she'd appeared normal most of the day. He gave her an injection to try and save her life, but my little sparrow died half an hour later, very quietly, on her hot-water bottle.

She had been with me three and a half years. My constant tiny companion, she was full of character; a wonderful little bird, who taught me a great deal. Always cheerful, affectionate and amusing, she seemed perfectly content with her life in my room.

I buried her under a fallen tree at the side of the field in a small Christmas box with holly leaves on it. It was the only one my kind friend, Janet, who comforted me, could find. Eric was out at the time. I missed Chirpy terribly. It was as if a tiny part of me had died too.

4

CLARA THE DOVE
AND AN IDEA

My husband being away a good deal, the room seemed empty as never before. I had little heart for painting or writing and spent a most unhappy winter mourning the loss of my little sparrow. February came, wet and dismal, and my friend Pam, who lived about five miles away, asked me if I'd like one of her little collared doves to look after. She and her son, Steve, ran a wild-bird hospital and the injured dove was getting rather water-logged and muddy in one of their outside aviaries, as, due to a damaged wing, the dove couldn't fly to get off the ground.

'I know how much you miss Chirpy,' Pam said. 'And the dove really needs to be indoors.'

I nodded. I could see she thought the collared dove and I needed each other.

'All right.'

So Clara, as I called her, came to live with us and the next day I set about making her a cage; Chirpy's old budgie cage was obviously far too small. In the local do-it-yourself shop I bought the materials I needed, having spent part of the previous evening designing what I hoped would be a suitable cage. I bought lengths of ¾ inch square wood for the frame, hardboard, Twilweld (strong ½ inch squared wire), Fablon and hinges, and so on, then I went home and got out the tool-box. It took me all the rest of the day and most of the following one to make that first cage. Most of the time I was kneeling on the floor of my room, sawing and hammering away until my arms ached; if not actual blood, there was plenty of sweat and tears as the wood split and some of my measurements proved inaccurate.

'Good heavens!' exclaimed Eric that second evening, 'What a mess.' Throwing down his coat he looked round hopefully for signs of his dinner, but there were none; I hadn't even got round to peeling the potatoes yet.

'Well . . . what do you think of it?' I sat back on my haunches with a weary sigh.

'Hmm . . . all right, I suppose.' Then, 'Er, where are the potatoes? I'll peel them.'

He was more interested in his dinner and I couldn't blame him. I was starving too. But the cage was finished at last. It measured 27 inches by 18 inches and was 18 inches deep. It had a hardboard floor and roof and the sides were hardboard halfway up and then Twilweld the top half, overlapping the hardboard by about two inches. Outside the cage I stretched pale blue Fablon across so that it showed through the wire upper half, giving a natural 'sky' effect inside the cage. The hardboard lower half was covered with brown 'wood-grain' Fablon inside, making it washable. The door was Twilweld in a wooden frame.

The idea was that perches could now be fixed across the cage, the ends sticking into the wire squares.

The cage finished – and Eric fed – I set about fitting it out. A couple of thickish perches, layers of newspaper, a covering of soil, a few clumps of turf, plus food and drinking bowls, and the cage was complete and ready for Clara.

Having lifted it on to a low table across the room from my bed I went to fetch her. The dove settled comfortably on one of the perches, closed her little round eyes, and fell asleep. Doves are not exactly live wires, I was to discover, and, apart from getting down to eat and drink, Clara seldom got off her perch during the days that followed.

Spring came at last and the monotonous chirping of sparrows early morning set me thinking of Chirpy again. How many other little sparrows were falling out of their nests and were perhaps being picked up by people who hadn't the time or knowledge to care for them properly? I'd already been told a sad story about a young blackbird that died in a box on top of a young couple's wardrobe; they'd left it there with only bird-seed in the box, not realizing it was a fledgling and needed feeding by hand. They were surprised to learn that a blackbird didn't eat seed anyway.

In bed, I listened to the sparrows and pondered on this subject. A week later, looking at Clara warm and dry and seemingly happy in her new home, I thought again about birds falling out of their nests or being caught by cats or hit by cars on the road. And I made up my mind. Reaching for a sheet of paper I wrote a few words and hurried off to the local newsagent down the road. 'INJURED WILD BIRDS

CARED FOR' read my ad., followed by my address and telephone number; we had a coin-operated telephone in the hall near the front door for use of the tenants.

'Well, Clara,' I said on my return. 'Now we'll see what happens.'

Next, I collected some suitable grocery boxes from near the dustbins. There were usually some there that had been discarded. I stacked these on top of my wardrobe outside the door – there was no room for it in the room – and then waited for my first patient.

= 5 =

ROOM FULL OF DUCKS

'YOU'VE done *what?*' said Eric next morning, wheeling round, razor in hand, from where he was shaving at the wash-basin.

'Put an ad. in. I'm going to take in injured birds.'

'You're mad! There's no room.'

I was afraid he was going to be like this. I gulped down some more tea, sitting on the end of his bed.

'I'll manage somehow. Just a few sparrows and things won't take up much room. I might get another little Chirpy, you never know.'

'You've got Clara . . . isn't that enough?' He buttoned his shirt, frowning.

'No, it isn't . . . she's such a dull old thing. Besides, I want to help other birds. Pam says lots get injured.'

'Well, I think you're crazy. There's little enough room for our belongings without bloody birds all over the place.'

Eric didn't share my enthusiasm for birds and animals, he preferred old prints and antique pots. I hadn't expected much encouragement in my new venture.

For a few days nothing happened, then one hot, sunny day I was eating my lunch of cold meat and salad when hurrying footsteps and frantic knocking on the door brought me to my feet. It was the housekeeper.

'Sorry to bother you, but could you come, please? The gardener from next door says there's a family of mallard ducklings in their garden and they're being attacked by the cats.'

Wiping my mouth I grabbed the largest box and followed her down the passage and out of the back door, pushing through a convenient gap in the privet hedge that divided the two gardens. Sure enough there was the mallard duck and eight baby ducklings huddled together against the front of the house on a narrow flower-bed. The duck was

23

quacking and obviously alarmed by the little group of people standing round watching, and the ducklings clustered round her, squeaking shrilly as I approached.

'Two of the ducklings have already been taken,' someone said.

'Yes,' added the old gardener. 'Cat's 'ad 'em . . . there was ten.'

The cats were half-wild and had been a nuisance in the neighbourhood for a long time. There were about ten of them in all.

We managed to get the eight remaining ducklings into the box but try as we did we couldn't catch the mother duck. The intention was to take the family to the river, where they'd be safe. If they'd made their own way they'd have had to cross the busy main road and possibly been killed or caused an accident. Time and time again we nearly caught her, but always she somehow managed to give us the slip. Quacking and distraught, she was obviously torn between staying with her brood and making her escape. Suddenly, taking us by surprise, the duck took off and flew low down the driveway, across the road and disappeared from sight.

Panting down the drive after her I gave chase, searching everywhere, but there was no sign of the duck. She must have flown right away. No one seemed to have seen her. Sadly I returned to where the ducklings were still squeaking in the box, picked them up and carried them indoors. Later I searched again, up and down the river and all around to see if I could see a single distraught-looking duck anywhere, but no luck.

I turned my attention to the eight little ducklings. They were pretty little things, chocolate and yellow, less than a day old and all squeaking their tiny heads off, obviously missing the warmth and comfort of their mother. Looked like I'd got myself an instant family. Whatever would Eric say? Eight!

I prepared a small box with a nest of hay in one corner and popped them inside, covering them with a very soft blue woolly hat that had seen better days. They were so small I could hold all eight in my two cupped hands. The family settled down to sleep, now warm and cosy, and the insistent 'pss-pss-pss' noises stopped; no doubt the little things were tired out after their ordeal.

I went into the hall to phone. 'What do I feed eight baby mallard ducklings on?' I enquired of our local RSPCA inspector seconds later.

'Chick crumbs,' said he, helpfully. 'They usually do very well on them.'

'Thanks.'

I hurried round to the corn merchant and bought a large bag of the crumbs – a fawn-coloured granular food. I didn't know it then but I should have bought shares in the stuff.

'Mix it to a crumbly consistency,' the shopkeeper told me. 'Not too sloppy, not too dry.'

Back home 'pss-pss-pss' noises were coming from under the hat and there was slight movement; my new family had woken up. And they were hungry.

They were slightly reluctant at first but within ten minutes I had all eight ducklings eating, wriggling their little beaks in the mixture, the air rent with their shrill cries. Afterwards, they fell asleep under the floppy hat again.

Later I made them a pen down the side of the room. It consisted of the box they were in with a small door cut in the side – so that the flap could be open or closed – leading into a larger box, forming a run. I spread newspaper in this, then added soil, a clump of turf, shallow paddling bowl and another dish of chick crumbs. The ducklings soon made full use of these facilities and I smiled on them benignly, pushing the thought of how on earth I was going to cope with eight large ducks – they'd grow large one day, wouldn't they? – right out of my mind.

But I was still worried about what Eric would say . . .

He said quite a lot when, dashing in for a quick cuppa, he saw them for the first time.

'Eight? How can you possibly keep eight large ducks in this small room? It's ridiculous!'

'Well they're not large yet, are they? They're tiny little things . . . ever so sweet. Just look at them.'

'They may be sweet now but you've got to think of when they grow big. What then? This room isn't big enough to swing a cat in.'

'I'll cross that bridge when I come to it,' I said firmly, coining one of Eric's favourite expressions. 'Anyway, what else could I do? I couldn't leave them to die, could I?' I'd told him how the mother mallard flew away.

'Oh well, it's up to you. I just hope they won't make an awful mess; they probably *will*.'

When the ducklings were four days old I took them for their first swim. Carrying them out on to the lawn I filled a Polythene washing-up bowl with water and set it on the grass inside a circular wire-netting enclosure I'd made, putting a couple of bricks in front of the bowl as 'steps'. At first they were scared but within minutes all eight had climbed in and were bobbing about like tiny boats obviously thoroughly enjoying themselves. From then on I took them outside for a swim every day and afterwards they scampered around on the grass like excited children.

By the time they were three weeks old the ducklings measured about ten inches long and had tiny black and brown feathers. Their appetites had grown accordingly and I made frequent visits to the corn merchant for more and more chick crumbs. They were having Bemax every day, too, now, and eating quite a lot of green food.

As the family grew I extended their pen foot by foot down the side of the room until it stretched under the small table supporting Clara's cage and eventually underneath the larger table we had our meals on. I had to make it narrower under the latter or our legs would have actually been in the pen as we sat at the table; while this might not have bothered me I didn't think Eric would take kindly to the ducklings nibbling his feet while he ate his dinner.

I also introduced a large rectangular Polythene bowl that held six gallons of water as an indoor swimming-pool.

One day Eric came home and found me clapped out, puffing and blowing, in a chair, surrounded by gallons of water in containers.

'Now what have you been doing?' he asked in amazement. 'What's all this for?'

'The ducklings,' I gasped, wiping perspiration from my face. 'It's water from the lake.'

'Good Lord.' He shook his head in disbelief, staring at the canisters. 'But why? What's the matter with the tap water?'

'It's so hard . . . I was afraid it might harm them in some way.'

This was true. Every day I walked across the field to the lake and staggered back with eight gallons of water; six for the new pool, one for drinking and mixing with their food, and a bucketful of water containing live daphnia, pond weed and so on which they loved to dabble in. It took four trips and, looking back, I can't imagine how I kept it up, day after day, for weeks. There was a heatwave in progress – the hottest summer for many years as the temperature soared – and this, along with the rock hard, parched field, made it doubly exhausting. But I was determined that my ducklings were going to have the best I could possibly give them.

How they loved that lake water in their dabbling bowl! As soon as they saw it newly filled each day they made a mad rush, clambering all over each other in their eagerness to dabble in that delectable weed, squeaking excitedly all the while. Watching them made all the hard work worthwhile.

Other bird patients had started to come in, among them a robin with a damaged leg. He was fascinated by the ducklings and took a great interest in everything they did in my room, and later, when he was released, in the garden. He used to perch on their pen, head on one side, watching them, and during the weeks that followed he was never far away.

When they were about a month old I introduced my growing family to the large plastic paddling pool I'd acquired on the lawn, having first arranged a wire-netting enclosure round it that was about three feet high and gave them space to run around on the grass, in between swimming. The pool was six feet in diameter and about one foot deep. The ducklings loved it and spent more and more time out there in the garden as they grew older. Round and round they paddled, diving and swimming like small seals under the water, sometimes for several minutes without surfacing. In between times they tore round and round on the grass chasing each other, jumping in and out of the water like happy kids.

One duckling in particular was getting very tame. He liked to sit on my knee and be stroked and made a fuss of. I called him Donald, though of course at that stage there was no knowing which sex any of them were.

The ducklings were getting very noisy at night now, tapping on their much enlarged sleeping quarters with their beaks at all hours and emerging long before dawn to hurl themselves into the water. The squeaking, tapping and splashing that went on was keeping me awake; what could I do?

In one of the three brick-built sheds at the back of the house I had a very large rabbit hutch; Eric had made it some time ago for my equally large rabbit – a white Beveren, now deceased. At the moment it was occupied by a small grey rabbit called Rosie. It was big enough for a baby elephant – well, almost – and I decided that if I moved Rosie into the much smaller hutch I also had in the shed the large one would make satisfactory sleeping quarters for the young mallards.

So what I did was this: every night one rather niggly little grey rabbit was transferred to the small hutch and the large one was prepared for the ducklings with a sheet of thick Polythene and a thick wad of newspapers, plus hay for bedding. This done, I fetched the ducklings – four at a time, they were getting very heavy – and installed them in the shed for the night. In the morning the large hutch was cleaned out and dried and Rosie and her bedding reinstated. Eight large mallards can make an awful lot of wet mess in one night and the project kept me pretty busy.

Every morning around 7 o'clock I filled their swimming-pool outside with fresh water from the hose, having drained and cleaned it the previous evening. The ducklings watched this operation with excited anticipation through the open doorway of the shed; how they loved that early morning swim! They could hardly bear to wait to be carried out.

One morning, when they were six weeks old, I went to collect my family from the shed and found them all spattered with blood. Fortunately the cuts were only superficial and I soon discovered the culprit – one of the young mallards was pecking the other seven. Once on the pool, Pecky Pete as I called him swam around pecking any duckling within reach, doing the same thing when they later ran around on the grass.

From then on Pecky Pete had to be kept separate from the others; more problems. Now what should I do? Finally I worked it out: when the miscreant was in my room the other seven had to be outside swimming, and when they were indoors, Pecky Pete could go outside for his swim. But what about at night?

In the end I borrowed an old mynah bird cage from my friend Pam and put that in the shed. At night, poor Rosie rabbit now had to sleep in this while Pecky Pete had the small hutch, the other seven mallards being in the large hutch still, of course. It was rather small for her but I made it quite cosy and I like to think she didn't mind too much.

'You seem to spend your life juggling around with things in the shed,' Eric remarked one morning, and he was quite right – it certainly felt like that. It was all rather exhausting.

But I was terribly pleased to have successfully reared all eight mallard ducklings under such difficult conditions; I was both proud and very fond of my fine, healthy family. I'd named the others, now; besides Donald and Pecky Pete there was Dougal, Duggie, Denis, Dulcie, Dora and Daisy. I put coloured PVC rings on their legs so that I could identify them.

Donald, the largest of the eight, continued to enjoy sitting on my knee and sometimes I sat nursing him while watching television. One day, to my surprise, Eric said, 'Here, let me have him,' but Donald struggled and didn't like Eric's lap. When Pecky Pete started his criminal activities he, too, became very tame as he was often alone with me in the room while the others were out on the pool. Sometimes I used Donald or Pecky Pete as a cushion, lying on the divan bed for a quick nap with the soft, feathery body as a pillow. They never moved or seemed to mind in the least.

When they were seven weeks old – fully fledged but with their flight feathers still growing – the young mallards had their photograph taken for the local paper. One exceptionally hot morning – the heatwave was still in progress – I was doing my chores in an old pair of shorts and a T-shirt, perspiration trickling down my red shiny nose, when there was a knock on the door. Outside stood a young man with a camera and a slim girl looking cool and lovely dressed in spotless white, with a white band round her not-a-hair-out-of-place blonde hair.

'Good morning,' they said. 'We've come to see the ducklings and photograph them.'

I was taken aback. I wasn't expecting them that morning and the room was in an awful mess, the duckling pen looking just about its dreadful worst. Like me . . .

'Please come in,' I said weakly, with sinking heart. I felt like Cinderella suddenly confronted by the late Princess Grace. But it would be nice to have some good photographs of the family, I cheered myself up thinking. The girl reporter sat down and asked questions, scribbling notes, while the young man capered around with his camera. Not that there was much room for capering, floor space being at a premium; there was less than two feet between my bed and the duckling pen. He wanted a picture of me cuddling Donald, but for the first time in his young life Donald declined; kicking and struggling, he made it quite clear that stifling hot morning that he didn't wish to be handled at all, thank you very much, and he made me out a liar for even suggesting that he liked sitting on my knee.

The young man darted outside and took a picture of the pen through the open window with the seven mallards waddling around; Pecky Pete was outside having a solitary swim. More photographs in the room, then we all trooped outside, me staggering with all seven ducklings in a box.

'Just watch how they all rush on to the water when I let them out!' I exclaimed, setting the box down inside the enclosure.

Poised with his camera, the young man waited for the rush. It never came. The ducklings waddled out slowly and stood around on the grass. Not one jumped into the water. I felt a fool . . .

'Well, they usually do,' I murmured apologetically. 'In fact, they always do.'

'I expect they're upset by the camera,' the girl in white suggested.

'Yes, that must be it,' I agreed.

We had to positively coax them on to the water and eventually the photographer got his pictures, including one of Donald . . . or was it

29

Duggie? . . . or Dougal? standing up in the water flapping his wings. When the photograph appeared in the paper they had him down as Pecky Pete. Oh well . . .

Naturally they all flatly refused to swim under water. My family seemed quite determined to be thoroughly unco-operative. I think they resented their peaceful routine being upset; it was all a bit much on a hot day. After a few more photographs the girl and the young man departed and the ducklings relaxed, swimming round and round under water. I went inside for a consoling long cool drink and left them to it. That evening as Donald nestled quietly and comfortably on my knee I stroked his sleek head and whispered, 'You were rotten this morning, Donald. Why didn't you do this then?'

Midsummer and the mallards were eight weeks old with their flight feathers complete, give or take a feather or two. They were all still mottled brown, of course; the males wouldn't get their colourful drake's feathers until their first moult in the autumn. They could fly now and they were getting restive. I knew the time had come for their release.

One lunchtime I got Eric to help me carry them, four at a time, across the field to the lake.

'They're heavy, aren't they?' he gasped as we had a short rest halfway. The field was still parched and cracked and it felt more like crossing the Sahara desert. The young mallards were much larger than the average river ducks, too.

Over at the lake I lifted the first four out of the box and set them down at the water's edge, down the shallow end. 'Go on,' I urged. 'It's lovely.'

They stood there dithering on the edge, quacking and afraid, and no amount of coaxing persuaded them to enter the water. 'Go on, Donald,' I said. 'Be brave!' But they still went on standing there, huddled together.

'Let's go back for the others, then,' suggested Eric, glancing at his watch. It was his dinner hour and he hadn't much time.

'All right.'

We went back and fetched the other four; the first ones still hadn't moved. I stayed with them while Eric went back to the house to grab a quick sandwich before getting back to work.

It was over half an hour before the ducklings ventured on to the water, first one and then the other seven eventually taking the plunge. With a lump in my throat I watched the little posse of eight swim away across towards the other side.

The lake looked beautiful, as always, with the large clumps of yellow iris in full bloom and reflected in the water and a sea of buttercups across in the pony field. I saw other mallards and a family of coots and I was pleased my youngsters would have company. With one last glance, they seemed fine, I turned for home carrying the empty box . . .

Later that day I returned to see how they were getting on, and saw them diving and dabbling among the pink and yellow water-lilies further down the lake. I was worried about whether they'd find enough food, though, so every day I went over there twice a day with a large dish of chick crumbs.

'I hope they'll be all right,' I said to Eric that evening. 'They came out of the water and ate the chick crumbs as if they were starving.'

'Of course they'll be all right . . . they're just greedy, that's all,' he insisted.

But I was worried; supposing they didn't know how to get food? After all, they hadn't any mum to teach them? I continued to take food over, and each time when I called the young mallards swam over, clambered out and gathered round the dish of crumbs, the mixture disappearing in seconds.

A few days after their release I was over at the lake one hot, sultry afternoon when the ducklings all climbed out and followed me round the lake waddling behind me in single file as I ambled along the narrow, winding path through the lush vegetation that bordered it. Down the far end I sat and rested awhile on the bank. Some of the ducklings slipped into the water, floating close by like boats at their moorings while the others remained with me, squatting down and sleeping by my side, heads under wings. I was rather touched by their affection still, but I suppose I was just a kind of mother figure – someone they felt safe with. The sun was hot and I leaned back, closing my eyes, momentarily feeling at peace with the world. I was sorry when I had to go back.

Gradually I gave them less food, firstly only taking one lot of chick crumbs a day and then cutting that out too and just taking bread. They seemed to be doing all right; I felt happier, now, about them.

One morning, however, after the family had been on the lake ten days, I walked over there and could only see seven ducklings. I searched around, but there was no trace of the eighth. I was worried about this; where could it be? Two and half weeks later, three more disappeared and again there was no trace; Pecky Pete and Donald were two that had vanished. I was very upset; where had four young mallards disappeared to in so short a time? The anglers there said they knew nothing; they hadn't seen or heard anything untoward. There were no feathers or clues of any kind to suggest that a fox or some other predator might have taken them either.

'Don't worry – they're probably all right,' said Eric without much conviction, but I was dreadfully worried.

I lay awake at night trying to figure it out. One possibility was that they might have flown somewhere, but if so why? They had always been together and kept close to each other on the lake. It wasn't spring and the breeding season. Knowing them as I did I felt this seemed unlikely, somehow. Had they been taken by foxes . . . or poachers . . . or one of the tramps living further up the field? Or by the squatters in the big house that overlooked the lake from a hill the other side? Or had the anglers removed them, perhaps thinking that the sudden influx in the wildfowl population might endanger their lines or disturb the young fish they stocked the lake with?

I didn't know; all my extensive enquiries drew a blank.

Two weeks later, with the last four young mallards still together on the lake, Eric and I went on holiday. I was very reluctant to leave them but my husband badly needed the break and everything had been arranged. A friend of mine, Trish, agreed to keep an eye on them.

'Don't worry, I'll go over there at least every other day and take them some bread so they won't feel neglected. Now go and enjoy yourselves, and *don't worry*!'

But of course I did worry . . . the whole fortnight.

The evening we returned I ran upstairs to see Trish. 'They're okay. I was over there yesterday. They're fine,' she assured me.

Early next morning I dashed over to the lake. They'd gone; there was no sign anywhere of the four ducklings. I searched everywhere but there was no trace; there wasn't one mallard of any description on the lake.

Feeling utterly desolate I sat on a fallen log and cried.

I never saw any of my beautiful mallards again, though whenever I was near any stretch of water I scrutinized the wildfowl population for signs of them and went on doing this for years. In my darkest moments I think about them and feel sure they were killed. But in brighter ones I like to think all eight are still alive and well . . . somewhere.

=6=

BLACKBIRDS EVERYWHERE

'DARLING, have you seen the salad bowl?' The voice came from Eric's room, where the bowls were kept in a cupboard.

'Er, which one? Isn't it in there?' I yelled through our two open doors.

'No, it isn't. The cut-glass one. You know, the one we usually use for lettuce and things.'

I came into the room and peered inside the cupboard. 'Here, this one will do.'

He wasn't going to be put off, though. 'But I'm looking for the other one we always use. It can't have disappeared.'

It hadn't disappeared; I knew exactly where it was. It had been turned into a bird-bath. Gulping, I gave it to him straight.

'What!'

'You see,' I went on hurriedly, 'I couldn't find anything else suitable ... well, not at the time. And it was just the right size for the blackbirds.'

Well, honestly!' he exploded. 'Bloody birds!'

'I'll wash it. It'll be all right if I give it a good scrub.'

'No!' He was truly horrified. 'I suppose this other thing will have to do.' He sloshed the lettuce about in the sink, muttering nasty things about my growing family.

I'd had quite a few blackbirds brought me while rearing the ducklings as well as several sparrows and a song-thrush. Blackbirds in particular seemed very accident prone, insisting on flying low in front of cars or getting seized by cats when fledglings. Sadly the cat victims often died of shock but I did what I could, the procedure being to keep them warm, quiet and covered up in a box with hay or a soft woolly hat or jumper until they showed signs of recovery or squeaked for food.

I had several memorable blackbirds brought to me. One was an

33

adult male and another a young female about six months old. I called them Beaky Bill and Edna. Beaky Bill had been reared by the lady who brought him. 'He's quite tame but he can only fly a few feet,' she told me. 'It wouldn't be safe to let him go, would it?'

'No,' I agreed. The blackbird looked very bedraggled with the tattiest tail I'd ever seen and a slightly damaged wing. 'Maybe he'll be able to fly better after he's moulted and got new feathers.'

Edna had similar wing damage. She, too, had been reared by someone and was fairly tame.

I had a third blackbird I called Bertie that I'd rescued from a cat and reared myself.

The antics of these three birds kept me amused and interested for weeks. They were all so different. Bertie slept at night in an old budgie cage – not Chirpy's, another one – and of course it was far too small for him now he'd grown big. But he loved this cage and spent a good deal of time in there in preference to somewhere larger.

People frowned and gave me a funny look – or so I imagined – when they saw an almost fully grown blackbird on the solitary perch in the budgie cage, and my sister, more forthright, expressed their looks in words one day.

'Fancy keeping that poor bird in there!' she exclaimed during a visit. 'It's *much* too small – poor thing!'

'I know it's small but he won't go anywhere else, honest. He really loves it in there.'

I could see she didn't believe me and I had to admit Bertie did look ridiculous in there.

Anyway, Bertie had now apparently fallen madly in love with Clara, the dove, and he had taken to sleeping in her cage at night. He went in there quite a lot during the day, too, jumping on to the same perch and sidling close to her. If he came too close Clara, a crotchety old thing at times, gave him a sharp peck and told him to keep his distance, but I was amused to see that he crept closer, almost touching her, when she dozed off to sleep. He also took refuge in there when Beaky Bill or Edna annoyed him, which was often; he didn't think much of either of them.

Beaky Bill was the staid, thoughtful type, I decided. He spent a good deal of his time up on the high inch-wide perch I'd fixed across the alcove, over the chest of drawers, watching all that went on in the room. As an adult male I think he felt a cut above the other two rather frivolous birds.

Edna, on the other hand, was a positive live wire and full of fun. She got into every kind of mischief imaginable. Like Kweekie, she loved flying around with any small movable objects she could find, dropping them all over the place. She also liked swinging on the shade of the central ceiling light, deliberately flying at it over and over again and making it swing so violently that I was sometimes afraid she'd bring it crashing down. She also pulled flowers out of vases, played around with small dishes and cutlery on a laid-up table, poked her head in jugs of milk, pecked the butter, stood on a kettle that was boiling on the gas-ring and generally caused havoc around the place.

All three blackbirds were now sleeping in Clara's cage at night and this led to a great deal of squabbling and messing about. Beaky Bill always roosted on the same corner perch, looking very solemn and superior; it was Edna and Bertie who always seemed unable to make up their minds who should sleep on which perch.

Clara was getting fed up with all this carry on in her cage and it was obvious something had to be done about it. So I fixed her up temporarily in a cardboard cage on the floor. It was in the corner under the window, where the ducklings used to sleep when they were small, and it was partitioned off from their long pen but leaving her a small run of her own, should she wish to walk about. Clara settled in her new ground floor flat quite happily and seemed to enjoy the renewed peace and quiet. A few feet away the growing ducklings ran up and down, and overhead the blackbirds quarrelled, but she snoozed on.

One afternoon a few days later I came in from the garden and couldn't find Bertie anywhere. I looked all round the room but there seemed to be no sign of him. Puzzled, I stood still and listened . . . then I heard him; Bertie had found his beloved Clara and was perched beside her in the cardboard cage on the floor. Very close in the half-dark down there, he was twittering away a little sub-song that he reserved for his favourite dove, while Clara with her dead-pan expression completely ignored her young admirer; as usual.

One day Beaky Bill decided to take up swimming as a hobby – or so it seemed. At that time I had an aquarium standing on the chest of drawers near the door; it was two feet by one foot and a foot deep. A large cold-water catfish called Catty lived in this tank; I'd had him ten years and I was very fond of him. He was six inches long now, with a wide grinning mouth and 'whiskers'.

On this particular morning Beaky Bill jumped down from his favourite perch overhead and started dithering on the edge of the tank, fluttering his wings and repeatedly dipping his beak in the water as he sidled up and down. Then he jumped across, turned round to face the water and did another little dance, repeating this performance several times.

I watched, fascinated. Bill had never liked the bird-bath – or should I say, Eric's favourite salad bowl – in which the other birds regularly bathed, and I'd never known him take a bath.

'Go on, Bill, go on!' I encouraged.

Next minute he jumped into the ten inches of water feet first, going right under, his black legs dangling down. Then, wings outstretched, he scrambled up the other side, shook himself like a wet dog and then turned round and jumped in again. Five times he did this, the water splashing out in all directions – I was glad Eric was out! – and he got really soaked; so did the surroundings. Meanwhile Catty lay low at the bottom of the tank, just his mouth and whiskers showing as he looked out from his 'house' – an inverted plastic flower-pot holder with a piece cut out as a door. Never in all his ten years had he seen anything like *this* before!

From that day on the intrepid Beaky Bill plunged in and out of the tank every morning, sometimes as many as six or seven times. I had to surround the tank with thick newspaper as he displaced so much water. Sometimes it took several large jugs to top it up. But he obviously thoroughly enjoyed these daily dips.

'What's all this water on the floor?' asked Eric, coming back unexpectedly one morning. He'd popped in to fetch something.

'That? Oh, er, something got upset.' Bill had beaten me to it that day and I hadn't slapped the newspaper down in time.

'Well I should mop it up, the floor's soaked.'

Another time he dashed in and said, 'The room seems to be full of blackbirds. Isn't it time some of them went?' before hurrying back to work.

I must say it did seem that way.

Edna was eventually released in the woods by the lake – her wing was all right now and she flew off into the trees quite happily. But Beaky Bill needed a little longer.

Bertie was ready to be released, too, but he wouldn't go. I tried to persuade him to fly off from my side window – 'Go on, Bertie. You'll like it out there!' – but the young blackbird seemed positively offended and, instead, flew down and sat with his Clara in the shadows. The second time I tried, a few days later, he flew straight into his old budgie cage and sulked there all afternoon – 'Why is she trying to get rid of me?'

A week later I tried again. This time Bertie flew back from the open window and down into Clara's box again. He spent a good ten minutes twittering to her, and I am convinced he was saying goodbye. Then he flew to the window sill and straight up into the trees. I had quite a lump in my throat again after witnessing this touching little scene, though I don't believe Clara was the least bit moved. She remained as sphinx-like as ever. Later I saw Bertie on the lawn. He seemed fine.

That just left Beaky Bill, but he wasn't to remain the only blackbird for long, for along came Bessie. She was a female and had been hit by a car; she had mild concussion but soon recovered. However, I wanted to keep her for a week or two under observation and to convalesce. Bessie and Beaky Bill hated each other on sight. Poor Bill, he'd been cock o' the roost for some time and now he was having his life plagued by a bossy female. Bessie chased him off his favourite perch and pecked him when he tried to return to it; she pecked him when he was about to take a swim and she pecked him when he went into the cage to eat. He was thoroughly henpecked, you could say, and he didn't like it one bit. I felt sorry for the poor fellow.

Beaky Bill, though, had now completed his moult and was resplendent with glossy black feathers and yellow beak – very different from the bedraggled bird he used to be. He could fly better now; not perfectly, but well enough. One day he started to sing and, having started, sang every day after that; not a sub-song, but a beautiful, full-throated blackbird song. He usually sang standing on one leg on his favourite high perch, Bessie permitting. It was a joy to hear; I felt very privileged.

One warm, sunny day I took Beaky Bill in a box across to the lake woods, where Edna had been released. He hesitated, then flew reasonably well into a tree. Now he'd have the lake to swim in! Bessie followed a week later. I felt a little guilty about this; what if she met up with Beaky Bill and started bossing him about again? Probably he never forgave me.

=7=

THE COMING OF WOL

THE conversation I'd had on the phone that morning left me elated; when the man and his schoolboy son laid a largish square box on the table I could hardly wait to open it. For inside was a baby tawny owl.

I'd never had, nor even seen, one before and it was love at first sight.

'I understand you found him in a field?' I asked the boy.

'Yes,' he replied. 'He was crouching at the bottom of a tall tree. I think he must have fallen out of a nest.'

Wol, as I called him, was about the size of a large grapefruit, fawny-white in colour, with tiny feathers just growing and visible through the thick covering of down. He blinked up at me from the box, his large round eyes appearing dark blue with long pale lashes and furry eyelids, the latter mottled, like his body. He had cream-coloured 'stockings' all up his legs and on his feet – the texture of a rabbit's furry foot, I thought – and a pale bluey-grey beak and matching toe tips, the nails being dark. He was about six inches tall. In all, he was about the sweetest thing I'd ever seen.

I picked up the little owl and so soft and cuddly was he that when I gripped him it was like gripping a ball of very soft wool. One couldn't feel any body at all – he was virtually as light as a feather.

I had fitted out Clara's cage for the baby tawny; Clara was now in an enlarged cardboard cage and seemed perfectly happy. Inside I'd placed a cardboard-box on its end with the top half open and the lower half closed, rather like a small stable door. Inside I'd made a bed of soft hay. I'd also cut a round hole in the side of the box as an exit to a thick branch I'd placed in the cage as a perch; I wasn't sure whether Wol was able to perch yet or not.

Gently I put the little owl in the box and he settled down in the hay, soon nodding off. He slept most of the day, waking occasionally for food, which I fed him now and again. I cut up small slivers of stewing

38

steak, which was all I had at the time, and popped some into his mouth. He took them daintily from my fingers, nodding off to sleep afterwards when he'd had enough.

Later, I tried Wol with chicken giblets, ox heart and raw mince, but he finally settled on sheep's heart as being his favourite food. So sheep's heart it was, from then on. Now and again I added a little roughage in the form of feathers, making a small meat and feather 'sandwich' and popping this into his mouth before he dozed off.

Unlike some young birds who stubbornly refuse to open their beaks even when hungry, on occasions, and spit out food popped in a reluctantly opened beak, the baby owl was never any trouble to feed. At night, though, he became restive and his fidgeting kept me awake. Quite obviously he didn't think much of a foster mum who lounged around in bed at night instead of going out hunting. Blinking at me from his box in the cage and uttering soft little cries, young Wol didn't understand it at all even though I filled his small tum with as much meat as he would take last thing at night before getting into bed. Sheep's heart was all right, he supposed, but where were the mice and nice plump voles? Gradually, however, he adapted, sleeping less during the day and presumably more at night.

After nine days Wol perched for the first time without wobbling over – he'd been very wobbly before – and I removed the cardboard-box to give him more room. He still continued to sleep at night on a little pile of hay in one corner of the cage, though, not roosting yet. His tail had grown to nearly three inches long from half an inch in ten days and his baby down was gradually being replaced by pretty mottled brown feathers. I noticed that he now sported a kind of black, bristly moustache growing down each side from the top of his beak. I also noticed he had a small bare patch just below the joint at the back of each leg, as if he'd worn out his elbows.

He was growing fast and I decided he'd soon need a larger cage. It was back to the DIY shop and out with the tool-box once more. This time I made a cage the same design as Clara's but very much bigger – owl-size – and heaved it on top of the other one, lifting Wol into his new house. Much better . . . he had plenty of room to grow in there.

Eric was as enchanted with the little owl as I was. 'What a beautiful little thing!' he'd declared the first time he saw him. Holding Wol in his large cupped hands he tickled his front with one finger and smiled at him.

'Yes, he's gorgeous, isn't he?'

I was glad he approved of Wol. Poor Eric, he'd had one or two nasty shocks recently, like the time he went to the fridge – kept in his room – for some milk one morning.

'What's *that*?' His raised voice echoed down the passage through the open door.

'What?' I asked, coming from my room to his with slightly sinking heart.

'That!' He stabbed a finger at the bottom shelf, frowning.

'Oh, that.' I was sorry he'd seen *that*.

'What *is* it? At the back there?' He was bent double like a croquet hoop, peering in at the back of the bottom shelf.

I gulped. 'It's . . . er . . . a bird.'

'A bird? What sort of bird? And what's it doing in the fridge?'

'It's a starling . . . a dead starling. It's all right,' I added hastily as he opened his mouth to speak, 'it's quite clean and I've got it sealed up in a plastic bag. Two bags, actually.'

He stared in disbelief. 'But, why?'

'Well you see, I'm going to take it to Pam's later . . . for Steve to do a post mortem. It has to be kept cold.' Her son was now at Veterinary College and was very interested in this sort of thing. He'd always been marvellous with birds.

I explained that young starlings had been dying like flies this year for no apparent reason and we wanted to know the cause. Eric was not amused, however.

'Well take it out . . . you simply *can't* keep dead birds in the fridge!'

He was grumpy for the rest of the morning and banged around muttering about the so-and-so birds taking over the whole place for several days.

The very same week Eric had reached for a tub of Blue Band margarine from the fridge and opened it to find maggots wriggling cosily in a bran bed.

'Joan! What are these maggots doing in here? I'm *not* having it!' he roared, chucking them down on the table. 'The fridge is for food. *Our* food!'

I sighed. If only he'd looked he'd have seen little holes punched in the lid and would have known it wasn't the marge.

So I was delighted he liked Wol.

Not that we were Wol's only admirers; he had many by now. Everyone wanted to see him. 'Aah! Isn't he *sweet*!' people bringing other bird patients cooed. 'How long have you had him?' Then, invariably, before they left it was, 'I wonder if I could bring my husband/son/old granny/auntie/niece/friend/neighbour to see him?' Sometimes it seemed they brought all of them.

But Wol wasn't in the least perturbed by visitors. He was cuddly and affectionate even with strangers and seemed to enjoy being tickled and stroked and having his head feathers ruffled. He was as gentle and friendly as a kitten and would play with my finger if I took hold of his furry clenched foot, fondling it with his beak. Everyone loved him.

After a few weeks the little owl had shed all his baby down and was clad in the barred fawn and whitish breast feathers of an immature tawny; next moult he would get his beautiful adult colouring. He had learned to fly and I began letting him out of his cage. His flight was silent, of course; owls have special soft tips to their flight feathers which enable them to pounce silently on their prey in the dark. I noticed, though, that he always landed heavily with quite a thud and I learned that nature arranged this so as to facilitate the demise of the victim by crushing it, if possible, as the owl landed.

Young Wol became a television addict, perching on the open cage door or on the back of a convenient chair with his dark eyes glued to the screen, head rotating clockwise in the way owls have. Television really fascinated him. He preferred things with plenty of action, mind you, such as a good cops-and-robbers car chase, quickly getting bored with people just talking – don't we all? After a while he'd fly up on to the high perch – Beaky Bill's favourite – and have a snooze, or sit there watching everything going on in the room. He was always terribly interested in all our activities and never missed a thing. Sometimes he lay right down on the perch, both ends of him virtually hanging over each side like a floppy cushion that had been draped over it. He looked most comical.

Wol had a habit, too, of suddenly pouncing on an imaginary mouse, or that's what it looked like. His head would start to rotate, eyes focusing on a spot on the carpet and then, with wings spread wide, he'd descend by gliding swiftly and silently to the floor, gripping something non-existent with his strong talons and making a great show of pecking at it. On investigating there was never a thing to be seen – not even a fly! I presumed he was just practising. Once he did catch something – a spider – and flew quickly to the teapot, his favourite perch, with the creature still clutched in one foot. He perched there for some time, holding the spider up in his clenched foot while standing on one leg in the usual owly fashion. He always took his time over this

41

sort of thing, mulling things over. Occasionally he bent his head to fiddle with the spider with his beak, then straightened and appeared to go off into a trance, staring blankly across the room. Minutes ticked by and then an amusing thing happened; the spider somehow made its escape, wriggling free from between his toes, but Wol, his mind elsewhere, didn't notice. A few seconds later it was a question of, 'Oh well, I think I'll eat my spider now,' as he unclenched his furry foot; then he stared – no spider! His expression clearly said, 'That's funny, I could have sworn I'd caught one.'

This sort of thing happened quite frequently and always amused us. He was a funny little owl.

'Tawny owls are so *thick*,' Pam once said. 'Anything but wise!' And I was beginning to see what she meant.

After I'd had him about five weeks Wol took to settling on the back of my armchair in the evenings, often lying down flat. Sometimes he would preen my hair, lifting a foot to get a gentle grip on a lock of hair – he never hurt – and then fiddling about with his beak among the strands. It was quite a pleasant sensation though rather tickly and somewhat distracting if one were reading. Now and again he did his pouncing-on-the-carpet act or got down and played with my foot. Sometimes he perched on my head – or Eric's – and he especially liked to watch television from the former vantage point these days.

To amuse our Wol I'd sometimes do things like blow a soft feather into the air; very solemnly he'd watch it float to the floor and then pounce on it. Or I'd give him a tissue to hold in one foot and tear into shreds with his beak.

One day a professional photographer called to take photographs of Wol for a trade magazine. They wanted an owl to represent 'wisdom'. He behaved beautifully, posing nicely in his open cage and not minding the flashes in the least. Wise he may not have been but he was certainly very photogenic; the black and white photographs were such a success that the young man came again next day to take some colour ones. They sent me enlargements of both. In one of them Wol appeared to be sucking a raised foot, his eyes rolled back. He looked more like the village idiot than a wise owl, I thought.

= 8 =

STIKKI

ONE day when Wol was about three months old a friend of mine who bred canaries rang up and said, 'I wonder if you could take a young kestrel? A chap brought him in. He's got something wrong with his legs – one's broken or something – and he can't stand.'

'Bring him round,' I said, 'and I'll see what I can do.'

The young male kestrel was a pathetic sight. Small and obviously only recently fledged, he had one leg tightly bound. But the leg wasn't broken. The kestrel was completely crippled with what appeared to be a chronic case of rickets. I was later told by a gentlemen I wrote to at the Falconry Centre that it sounded to him like an acute lack of calcium, resembling rickets.

The young kestrel was unable to stand because both legs were bowed and resembled the letter O as he sat back on his tail, his useless legs stuck forward. His toes were screwed up and quite useless too.

I prepared a box, placing it on its side with a makeshift wire front, so he could see out. No perches were necessary, of course, but I put a thick covering of hay at the bottom and propped the poor kestrel upright, making him as comfortable as possible. I had to stand the box on the chest-of-drawers in Eric's room as I'd run out of space in mine. I hoped he wouldn't mind and I awaited his return from work with some trepidation. I'd had to shove up a few priceless old Oxfam bargains – what on earth *was* that peculiar metal thing? and that queer wooden object? – to make room.

The kestrel wouldn't eat at all unless forcibly fed, but whether this was because he'd never learnt to feed himself or because he was too unhappy I never knew; I was inclined to think it was the latter. When consulted the vet had prescribed a daily dose of Abidec, a very good liquid form of concentrated vitamins, and exercises for his legs several times a day. Plus regular feeding, of course.

Wol, meanwhile, had decided he liked ox heart, so I started feeding the young kestrel this, taking him on my knee, opening his beak and putting slivers on his tongue. He was very co-operative and never made any fuss, swallowing all I gave him, including the hefty dose of daily Abidec. Three times a day I got him out to do his exercises, getting him to try and use his legs and flap his wings.

Stikki, as I called him, gradually responded to treatment and grew stronger and after eight days I was really thrilled when he stood for the first time. He was very shaky and his toes were still clenched but it was a marked improvement and one I'd scarcely dared hope for, especially so soon. Three weeks from when he came he was standing normally, his toes now straight, and he was perching, preening and feeding himself. I was delighted; people who had seen the poor kestrel when he first arrived could scarcely believe it was the same bird.

'What a difference!' exclaimed Kay. 'You have done well with him.'

'Yes, I'm very pleased with him. But of course his legs will always be slightly bowed.'

'Still, he can stand and perch and fly . . . I think it's wonderful.'

Eric liked Stikki and didn't seem to mind him in his room, thank goodness. The young kestrel had become very tame. He was always gentle even in his initial distress, and I never had to wear gloves to handle him. Eric used to chat to Stikki while he was dressing in the mornings and allow him to perch on his hand sometimes – an honour indeed!

I was pleased, too, that Wol and now Stikki liked ox heart; larger, leaner slices meant there was less waste. Neither bird would eat fat so it all had to be cut off.

Clara had gone on her summer holidays back to Pam's aviary, so that meant I could move Stikki into her cage, back in my room. I had wondered whether to try him in with Wol but I wasn't sure if they'd get on and I didn't want to risk a fight at this stage. Clara's cage – it was always to be known as this – was really too small for Stikki, though; what should I do?

'Make a new one, then,' suggested Eric, as if it were as easy as falling off a log. I didn't really enjoy carpentry and if anything had found the second cage even more difficult and frustrating to make than the first. But it didn't look as if *he* were going to volunteer.

'Looks as if I'll have to.'

Back to the DIY shop, and a new kestrel cage was eventually made and stacked high on top of the other two. It was roughly the same size as Wol's cage. Stikki seemed pleased with his new home, nicely fitted out with thickish branches from trees and hay, soil and turf covering the newspaper floor. He settled on the high corner perch, preened his feathers and then had a nap.

Some time later I acquired a very large and strong cardboard-box which made yet another cage. It was about three feet by two feet square. Staggering in from where I found it by the dustbins – someone must have bought a large television set, sound equipment or something – I prayed silently that it would fit into the space I had in mind. It would be touch and go I knew. Standing on a high stool I managed with great difficulty to heave the box on top of the other wooden cages and found to my relief that it just fitted in; there was exactly one and a half inches clearance between the top and the ceiling. Fitted out, this new cardboard cage was to prove very useful indeed for largish or 'resident' birds.

9

THE OWL
AND THE KESTREL

A week later Wol and Stikki met for the first time in my room. Opening both cage doors I sat back and watched, keeping very still. Both flew out into the room after a few minutes but to different perches, then, a few minutes later, both birds landed on the back of the other armchair. Standing about a foot apart, they turned and faced each other. They remained motionless, staring, but then Wol, deciding he'd seen enough, flew up to the perch over the chest-of-drawers. And that was that; they ignored each other for the rest of their time in the room. In the days that followed, they met several times but remained pretty indifferent to each other. Well, at least they weren't fighting.

A few weeks later, when they were both a little older – and wiser? – I tried Wol and Stikki together in the same cage, introducing the kestrel into Wol's cage rather gingerly. Wol disapproved. Puffing out his feathers to look twice the size and very fierce he advanced menacingly towards Stikki, sidling along the branch. Stikki took the hint and moved further away. Wol glared at him, blinking rapidly as he always did when nervous or upset, then as if suddenly losing interest he started preening, his feathers going back to normal again.

Gradually over the weeks the owl and young kestrel got used to each other and soon became firm friends, though Wol was always very much the boss. Never actually aggressive, he always got what he wanted by sidling close to Stikki and looking fierce and threatening, feathers puffed out. Usually what he wanted was Stikki's favourite perch. This posture was invariably enough; grudgingly the kestrel moved away, often returning later, however, in an attempt to regain his perch. But a few more withering looks from the owl usually sent him packing again.

One day, a friend caught some baby mice for the two birds of prey, handing me the dead creatures in a pot. I wasn't very keen on the idea – I like mice and felt sorry for them! – but I was persuaded that more natural food would do them good and make a change, once in a while. I handed one small mouse to Wol and another to Stikki, then stood back to watch what happened.

Wol transferred his mouse from beak to large feathered foot and held it like a lollipop, eyeing it. Then he started twiddling the tail with his beak, treating it more as a plaything than the delicacy it was supposed to be. Stikki, meanwhile, had gripped his small mouse firmly in one lean, yellow foot, pinning it to the branch he was standing on. Slowly and methodically he then set about eating it, tearing at the creature in the usual way without more ado.

After five minutes Stikki's mouse had gone and he was cleaning his beak on the wood. But my silly old owl was still twiddling the tail of his and hadn't even started. Stikki, mouseless, was now eyeing Wol's so I quickly gave him a second one which he dispatched in the same efficient way. I gave him a third mouse. Meanwhile, Wol, still clutching his first mouse, was now gazing into space, his mind obviously on other things. I think he'd forgotten he was still holding it; owls are like that.

'Now come on, Wol,' I coaxed, '*eat* it!' But it was half an hour before he obliged. Just when I was beginning to despair he opened his large mouth, popped the whole mouse in with his foot and swallowed it in one gulp, almost as if to say, 'Well, that's what you wanted, isn't it?'

Having got the hang of it he then ate two more mice fairly quickly in the same way.

Some weeks later I gave them some large, adult mice. Stikki ate his in the usual manner but Wol decided that they were tough old farm mice and definitely unfit for owl consumption. He stared at his for a long time, mulling things over; to eat or not to eat? Finally, slowly and extremely nastily, I thought, he decided to just eat the stomach. I moved away hastily, having no desire to watch further, but when I returned some time later I found what looked like a miniature mouse hearth-rug on the floor of the cage, its tiny legs splayed out and the head still intact. Wol, I gathered, had finished with it; it was all mine. He preferred ox heart for dinner, thank you very much . . .

The two birds had become almost inseparable now, flying round the room together and often perching side by side. Sometimes, of course, they quarrelled, as all friends do, but neither ever fought or drew blood though with powerful talons and strong hooked beaks they could easily have done so. It fascinated me to watch them, and even Eric put down his paper sometimes in the evening and said, 'Just look at Wol!' smiling and shaking his head at their antics.

Stikki became very playful as he matured and had certain toys he played with and was very fond of. His favourite was an ordinary stick which he took everywhere with him, round the room and in the cage, dragging it around the floor clutched firmly in one foot and flying with it all over the place; hence his name. It was sixteen inches long and about a quarter of an inch in diameter and was soon worn smooth and barkless with constant 'handling'. Many's the time I had to duck quickly as the airborne stick flashed past. His other toys consisted of an empty Smartie tube, a small rubber crab, a rolled up woollen sock, a plastic lemon and a red felt mouse. He liked me to pretend to take these things away from him and would make various ear-splitting noises as if in protest. If I stopped playing he would bring one of the toys near me again for the game to be resumed, his head turned sideways in the appealing way these birds have of looking at you when excited or feeling playful.

He was a dab hand as a goalie, too, and many's the exciting game of Plastic Lemon Football we had – he seldom let the lemon through when I bowled it at him, sitting back on his tail and tackling it with his feet.

Occasionally Wol would join in his games though as a rule he wasn't much of a one for romps on the floor. Nevertheless Stikki sometimes got him going and the owl would lumber round the room after the much more agile kestrel, usually attempting to get the woollen sock or red mouse.

When the evenings became colder Wol discovered the joys of warmth from our electric fire. Slowly and with much head bobbing he stalked right round the small bowl fire, pecking the back of it. Then he settled on the rug in front of it in a prone position, his head facing the element and inches away, his wings spread to their fullest extent, each feather splayed out to get the warmth. Head thrown back to get the heat on his throat, he'd close his eyes and remain motionless like this for such a long time we feared he'd burn his eyeballs or something, so close did he lie. We got used to the pungent smell of burning owl, however, and it never seemed to do him any harm apart from slightly scorching his head feathers on several occasions. When the heat became unbearable our funny owl sprang away with the special little noise he made if something hurt him, invariably returning minutes later for more punishment. He loved that fire.

48

About this time Wol indulged in his first bath; a great occasion, as he'd always scorned water and became really upset if some other bird bathing splashed him, as some young starlings once did. Starlings are fanatical bathers and never miss an opportunity to jump into the nearest dish of water. On this occasion I'd placed a green plastic cat-litter tray, which made a good bird-bath, on the floor for another bird and very much to my surprise my intrepid owl swaggered over in the way he had and stepped into the water, dipping his beak. He made no attempt though to flutter his wings and bathe properly. 'Go on, Wol!' I encouraged – I always seemed to be urging reluctant birds to do something – 'that's it.' But he just went on standing there as if uncertain what to do next. I agitated the water with one finger and made further encouraging noises, but still he just stood.

I had an idea. Fetching a jug of water I gave him a shower, trickling it slowly over his head. Wol loved it! Water trickling down his beak, he sprang into action, fluttering his large and beautiful wings and fluffing out his feathers as he repeatedly bobbed and ducked in the water; he really went to town! From then on Wol bathed several times a week but only – and he was adamant about this – *only* if someone supplied a shower to start him off. No shower, no bath. Once, busy doing some job, I saw Wol standing in his bath but I took no notice. Five minutes later I glanced across and he was still there, motionless, looking my way. Two minutes later he swaggered across the room with his peculiar rolling sailor's gait and gently nibbled my slipper, hurrying back to his green bath when I rose to my feet and reached for the jug; he blissfully enjoyed the desired shower.

Stikki liked the green bath too, but he bathed straight away, no messing about. Sometimes he got impatient with Wol, queueing up for a bath, but the owl wouldn't allow him near until he'd 'showered' and bathed, always taking his time.

The two birds of prey were very different in character. The owl was a dreamer, slow and ponderous, and the kestrel quicker witted and swift in his reactions. And of course the former was basically nocturnal, the latter diurnal. This sometimes led to problems at night. Usually Stikki went to bed first, mid-evening, and the cage was then covered. Last thing at night I'd lift the cover and pop Wol quickly inside, trying not to disturb the sleeping kestrel. Very occasionally Wol got fidgety in the night and moved around, softly hooting, but a curt 'Ssh, Wol!' from me usually shut him up.

Stikki had the most beautiful eyes, I always thought; so large, round and liquid and full of expression. Sometimes he'd perch quietly on my hand as we sat by the fire, staring into my face as I whispered to him.

'He's really fond of you, isn't he?' Eric once remarked, watching. Certainly I was very fond of him. Stikki would perch like this for a long time, quite relaxed, with his feathers fluffed out and his yellow feet with their needle-sharp black talons at rest on my hand, never gripping or hurting. Sometimes he'd carefully preen each feather while I watched, marvelling at the way each breast feather had one dark spot; never a feather with two spots or one with no spot at all. For now, of course, Stikki was a handsome male with a blue-grey head and chestnut back.

I was delighted with my owl and kestrel – they were both affectionate, charming and fascinating to study. They seemed very much at home and happy in their unusual surroundings, too. I had thought a good deal about whether either of them should one day be released to the wild, but had been advised against it. Stikki's legs would always be suspect and the Falconry Centre informed me that even a normal kestrel was capable of breaking a leg while descending on prey as there is so much stress involved. I thought he'd already suffered enough with his legs to risk this happening. As for Wol, he'd really got too tame for release. And I'd been told horrific stories about tawny owls being stoned even in this day and age and about them being unable to adapt well after captivity. Besides, I just couldn't see him perched up a tree waiting for some old mouse to pass by.

=10=

JACKO THE TERRIBLE

ONE Monday morning in February two young men brought me a jackdaw. One of them didn't say very much and the other couldn't; he had a bad stammer. So I was unable to find out much about the bird. All I could make out was that he was very tame and had therefore probably been hand-reared or someone's pet, and that one of the young men had found him locally and had him a few weeks. After they'd gone I realized they hadn't told me why they'd brought the jackdaw to me; he certainly wasn't sick or injured in any way. I was to find out the answer to this the hard way.

Within minutes of their departure it became apparent that Jacko, as I called him, was a home-wrecker and a rascal. During the five minutes I was in Eric's room looking for a suitable box to put him in the jackdaw pinched a box of matches and scattered them round the room, pulled the flowers from a vase and pecked the heads to pieces, removed and hid the whistle from the kettle, tore up a newspaper and pulled cutlery out of a box, to name but a few things. In that short time it seemed that Jacko had played with and abandoned just about every movable object in my room.

Full of life, he seemed to spend the entire day looking for destructive things to do. I began to wonder what I had taken on – and I realized why the young men had wanted someone else to have the bird. Jacko made it quite clear, that first day, that he'd got a mind of his own and that, for one thing, he didn't like being caged. I offered him the choice of two largish cages thoughtfully fitted out with all mod. cons. suitable for a jackdaw, but he declined both, going berserk when forcibly installed in either and obviously preferring his rampage round the room. As well as the wooden cages I had numerous cardboard ones now of varying sizes. All these had Twilweld doors, some opening sideways and some dropping downwards.

51

The jackdaw was a friendly fellow, with twinkling grey eyes and a tatty ragged tail and jaunty walk. He was obviously used to, and enjoyed, human companionship; he alighted on my shoulder every few minutes, his grey nape feathers erect as he tweaked my ear or pulled my hair. Then he darted away, hell-bent on rearranging my once tidy room; I prided myself on the fact that it *was* normally kept clean and tidy no matter how many birds I had, all the cages and boxes being cleaned out very frequently, most of them every day.

I wondered what to do about Jacko. It was obvious he couldn't ever be left alone in the room and he didn't like cages . . . so what? He appeared too tame for release and too used to being with people to fend for himself – or so I reasoned at the time.

Somewhat in desperation I fetched a small cardboard cage with a drop-down wire front and popped Jacko in this. Designed for small birds, it was little more than a foot square and had a single perch inside and a sheet of paper on the floor. It would do while I took a break, I told myself; I was quite exhausted with cleaning up after the bird. And something had to be done before Eric came in for lunch – he'd go mad if he found the room wrecked!

I flopped down in one of our two armchairs and closed my eyes, trying to think what to do. Suddenly I realized the room had gone strangely quiet. Looking up I saw that Jacko was standing sedately on the perch and appeared quite calm and happy; he actually liked it in there! It seemed rather odd that he preferred such cramped quarters to the larger cages offered but there it was. I left the room and when I returned ten minutes later I found that he'd dragged the sheet of newspaper from the floor of the cage and arranged it neatly as a 'blind' in front of him, leaving only half an inch open at the top of the wire door and making it impossible for me to see inside. Apparently he was asleep behind this as there was no sound from the cage.

Jacko loved this small cage and from then on it became his. Later I persuaded him to pass at least part of each day in one of the large wooden cages – the one I made for Stikki originally – but he always insisted on sleeping at night in the small one and also took his afternoon nap in there. I'd placed the small cage on top of Crusoe's cage as there seemed to be nowhere else to put it. Crusoe was an invalid crow I had – he lived in a much larger version of the cardboard cage Jacko favoured, with a drop down wire front. It was on the chest-of-drawers, near the door; sadly, Catty had died and I no longer had an aquarium up there.

This jackdaw cage on top of his didn't meet with Crusoe's approval at all. He didn't like the strange jackdaw up above and he kept twisting his head to try and see the new fellow and was thoroughly uneasy about it.

Jacko continued to manipulate the newspaper shutter at the flick of a beak when he wished for privacy, removing it again just as quickly if he wanted to look out or was feeling more sociable. It was so neatly done; never crooked or untidy. But I had to make sure he had tabloid newspaper not 'quality' paper as he got in a muddle with the latter, on one occasion, and spent a long and, I'm sure, worrying time getting it in the desired position.

Compared with Crusoe, Jacko was a very small and conservative eater. He liked small pieces of bread-and-milk, cake, cheese, peas, tomato, scrambled egg, baked beans and sometimes potato, but a few small bits would suffice. He didn't like meat of any kind, nor worms, but occasionally he'd accept a small morsel of cat food from a tin, provided it was of fish extraction and not meat.

The jackdaw could fly all right but in the room he usually preferred to walk everywhere, strutting around on the carpet and just jumping or flying upwards to get into some mischief elsewhere. He liked to 'help' me peel the potatoes in the sink, standing on my hand and catching the peel in his beak as it appeared. Sometimes he flew off with a small potato, pecking it to pieces in some quiet corner of the room before returning to the sink. I had never known a bird with such a permanent wicked twinkle in its eye – so intensely alert and on the look-out for something to play with or destroy. He never seemed to relax for one minute when out of the cage.

After I'd had Jacko a week I recklessly invited him out into the garden. It was a fine, sunny afternoon and I had an idea he'd come to me if I called him as he always did indoors and then I'd be able to bring him inside when I wanted to. Well, it sounded all right in theory . . .

It didn't work out that way, of course. I had a lot to learn. Jacko flew up on to the roof and stayed up there fooling around all afternoon. Playing around the chimney-pots and flying from eave to eave, he had a great time; sometimes he came down to a low part of the roof and peered down at me from the guttering, chattering away with the short, sharp barks he made when I called, 'Come *down!*' He was always very polite, answering whenever spoken to. On this occasion I was getting worried in case he alighted in the garden and one of the half-wild cats that were still around pounced on him. I began to wish I'd never let him out. Eventually, temporarily exasperated, I left him to it and started across the busy main road to post a letter. Next second there was a familiar plop on my shoulder and there was my naughty jackdaw; he'd decided to come with me. I was afraid he'd do something crazy, however, and perhaps get hit by a car or fly into someone else's garden or house, so having reached up and grabbed hold of him I turned back into the house and put him in his cage.

Jacko liked a bath and always took one in the wash-basin under a running tap. I tried to get him to bathe in a more conventional way, like the other birds, but he insisted on the wash-basin always. Afterwards, he liked to dry himself on the kettle or else fly up to the high perch.

He took a fiendish delight in teasing Crusoe, usually pecking him if they met. He'd stand very close to where the crow was perching in the open entrance of his cage – Crusoe's wire door was seldom closed as he liked to lean out, perching on the edge of the box – with some favourite article he knew Crusoe wanted in his beak, deliberately taunting him. Often it was a piece of sponge they both liked, or some other plaything. But he always stood *just* out of reach. Some people thought the jackdaw vicious because he liked to tweak your ear or peck fingers – and he hurt! – but to my mind he pecked people, and sometimes other birds, just for the hell of it and not out of any malice. He loved you to yell 'Ow!' and spring away; it was a good game, and Jacko loved a game of any kind.

One of his favourite toys was the cut-off finger of an old rubber glove; it had to be yellow – he took no notice of a pink one. This was known as Jacko's Yellow Fingy and he fetched it like a dog if you asked where it was, searching for it in all sorts of unlikely places until he found it. Often he perched in the small box with Yellow Fingy in his beak – not doing anything, just holding it. He loved it. When it became torn and grubby I cut off a new one for him; fortunately for Jacko I was forever tearing the glove of my right hand and of course there were four Yellow Fingys per glove, plus the thumb.

Another favourite toy was the whistle off the kettle and the first thing he did when let out into the room for a fly around early morning was alight on the kettle and remove it.

'Where's the whistle off the kettle gone?' Eric would say as he filled the latter under the tap. 'Has that damn bird taken it again? He's a menace!'

That damn bird usually had taken it; sometimes he hid it and it was missing for days, eventually turning up in some obscure place. But Eric liked Jacko and was as amused by his antics as I was. At first, anyway.

One day in early April I released Jacko in the woods by the lake. I had decided it was unfair to keep such a healthy and lively young bird a prisoner any longer, and now that spring had come I thought the woods would be the safest place for him, and, hopefully, he might meet others of his kind somewhere around. We'd grown very fond of him and I'd miss him dreadfully but I hoped I'd see him around over there when out walking.

Looking back I can see I really knew very little about jackdaws. What a lot I had to learn . . . the hard way!

Anyway, I left him pecking around under the trees; he seemed quite happy, prodding for insects in fallen trees. As I turned to go he gave me his cheery goodbye noise – it sounded just like 'Cheer-i-o!' on a rising scale – and I came home. I would go back frequently to make sure he was all right, I told myself.

Next morning I started off across the field to the woods to see if I could see him. I'd been worrying about him in the night as I knew I would. Eric's 'Oh, he'll be all right' – he always said this about any departing bird – did nothing to reassure me. When I was two-thirds of the way across I heard Jacko calling me: 'Cheer-i-o!' It was also his hello noise. I couldn't see him at first but as I entered the woods, squeezing through the layers of barbed wire, he flew straight to my shoulder. I could see at once he was glad to see me; he left me in no doubt that he had not enjoyed his night alone over there.

I brought him home, deciding that if he wanted to go on living with us I'd just have to try and give him more freedom, that was all. And from then on I took the jackdaw for a walk in the field every day.

At first I used to carry him out in his small box cage each afternoon and release him to fly or strut around. Glad of a rest, I usually sat on a fallen elm tree and watched but sometimes I took him to the woods and gradually he grew bolder and more daring – he'd been surprisingly timid out of doors. I noticed that to begin with he seemed only able to fly short distances and the first time he decided to fly low across the lake I had my heart in my mouth, not sure if he was going to make it. But soon his flying was normal.

The lake was very beautiful in the spring and, though I was busy again with bird patients, I tried to spare at least one hour to take Jacko on these daily jaunts. He was good company, too, always staying close. I took to having little picnics with him beside the lake; it was the closed season for coarse fishing so we had it all to ourselves. I took a flask of tea, biscuits, a small container of bread-and-milk for Jacko, and a rug to sit on, spreading the latter in a little clearing near the water's edge. While he flew or strutted about, poking his beak into everything everywhere, I sat watching young mallard ducklings on the lake, coot chicks, and other young birds. Sometimes I caught a fleeting glimpse of a kingfisher as it flashed from bank to bank, or the kestrel that always nested in an ivy-covered dead elm on one of the tiny islands in the lake. A pair of Canada geese was breeding there; the male bird, no doubt bored while his mate incubated the eggs, often swam across to eat the bread I threw, lingering nearby in case I had more. Sometimes I saw a heron, but usually he saw me first and flew off, or decided not to land. Invariably I felt a pang as I thought of the missing ducklings – the family I'd reared so lovingly and painstakingly.

Across the lake the ponies grazed in the large field that side. Now and then one would wade into the shallow water and drink. Jacko was afraid of ponies and always hid when this happened.

It was all very peaceful and relaxing especially after the hectic time I had back home. For Jacko's part he had the whale of a time, settling on my shoulder every now and then and accepting small morsels of bread-and-milk before flying off to amuse himself elsewhere. He never drank from the lake – he wouldn't – so I took along a small pot which I filled with water and from which he drank when thirsty. Sometimes I walked round the winding path to the opposite side of the lake and although Jacko would accompany me part of the way, perching on my shoulder or hand, he always flew back before we got right round. For some reason he didn't like the other side. On my return he was always waiting for me by our picnic spot with the usual cheery greeting.

One day when we were in the field and not by the lake Jacko apparently grew bored and flew off. Usually if I shouted he came back, but this time he didn't appear. I hadn't seen him go as I'd been lying on the grass with my eyes closed, enjoying the warmth of the sun.

I didn't know it then but this was the beginning of a new phase in Jacko's life; one that was to give me an awful lot of trouble and worry.

=11=

FURTHER ADVENTURES
OF JACKO

I FOUND him on the roof over the front door. Greeting me with what I took to be a glad cry, Jacko flew down on to my shoulder and we went indoors. Fine. Two days later, though, he disappeared from the field again and once more I found him on the same roof. This time, however, he refused to come in with me until much later. I kept going outside and calling but it was beginning to get dark when he decided to descend and let me carry him indoors. Not quite so fine. The third time he flew from the field he wasn't on the roof and I was just wondering where he could have got to when the house-keeper put her head out of the front door and said, 'Phone call for you.'

It was Eric, speaking from the garage. 'Hello, darling. Er, have you lost Jacko?'

'Well, yes. How did you know?'

'Because there's a jackdaw on the roof of the forecourt here. I thought it must be him. You'd better come at once. He's been chasing a crowd of schoolchildren down the road – swooping down on them and frightening them. You'd better come quickly!'

My heart sank. Jumping on my bike I dashed off down the main road the few hundred yards to the garage only to find that the jackdaw had disappeared again. 'He's gone that way,' said Eric, pointing further down the road. 'But that's where he was a few seconds ago,' he pointed to the roof, 'only we couldn't reach him or get him to come down.'

Giving chase, I caught up with Jacko near the railway bridge another hundred yards further on, managing to grab him off a fence. I cycled home with one hand on the handlebars and the other clutching the wayward jackdaw in a vice-like grip. 'You *bad* boy!' I chided him.

After this Jacko took to staying out all night, on occasions, returning early morning. We never knew where he went, though about a year later a young Spanish couple told me he entered their bedroom several times very early in the morning and gave them quite a fright. They were tenants in the house with a front room on the first floor and always slept with the window wide open. But at the time I knew nothing of this; nor did it explain where he spent the hours of darkness.

One night, very late, I was just about to close the curtains prior to going to bed when something fluttered against the window outside, dark and hovering. It was Jacko!

'Good thing we weren't watching a Dracula film!' remarked Eric. It was pitch dark outside and his wings against the latticed panes really did sound quite spooky; being black in colour, of course, I couldn't see him at first.

'Jacko! Where on earth have you been?' I said, ruffling his head feathers. Jauntily he walked to where his supper was waiting, the usual twinkle in his eye; he was very hungry.

Another evening he slipped in through my open window so quietly that Eric and I, watching television, didn't realize he'd returned until I saw him eating his supper on a small table behind us. But Wol saw him come in. He was on the high perch over the chest-of-drawers – instead of the aquarium we had a small portable television up there now. It was the owl's head rotating wildly that I noticed first; he was bending forwards, his eyes glued to Jacko behind us. He wasn't used to birds coming through windows at night! Wol and Stikki had never met Jacko in the room. Usually the jackdaw was in his cage – or missing! – when they were out in the room, and vice versa.

One very hot Sunday Eric and I were sitting in the field with Jacko.

'Must we bring Jacko?' Eric had complained. 'I want to be able to relax – not bother about him.'

'But he loves flying about and it's so hot indoors. I'm sure he'll be good,' I added, without conviction.

I felt hot and fidgety, though; unlike Eric, I really preferred sitting in the shade and there wasn't any, where we were near the fallen elms. It was baking. I decided to walk across the field to the woods and lake and then make my way slowly up to the top of the field in the shade of the trees. We could hear voices through a loudspeaker coming from a garden bordering the field up there and I thought I might take a peep at the garden fête obviously in progress through the fence.

No, Eric didn't want to come. 'I'm quite happy here,' he said. He was reading the Sunday paper, half dozing, in the chair he'd taken out there.

'Okay. Well, I'll take Jacko. It'll make a change for him from playing around here.'

Eric put down the paper, frowning. 'Do you think it's wise? You know what he's like.'

'Oh, he'll be all right. He likes a walk and a fly round.'

'Well don't say I didn't warn you,' was Eric's parting shot as he closed his eyes, revelling in the sun. The paper fell on the grass.

I set off slowly, Jacko on my shoulder and looking as good as gold. He flatly refused to fly at all but crouched there all the way up the field, much to my surprise, clinging like a limpet. Perhaps it was too hot for him, too? When we got to the high fence between the garden where the fête was and the field, however, Jacko left my shoulder and flew on to it; he, too, could obviously hear the laughter and music and merriment going on the other side. I was just looking for a suitable knot-hole to peer through when to my horror the jackdaw flew off the fence into the garden to join in, disappearing from view and leaving me unable to see or follow him. I called and called but no answering cry from Jacko this time. What should I do? And – a more disturbing thought – what was *he* doing?

I decided to walk back a little way and round the corner of the fence to see if I could see into the garden from there. Crawling through a hedge and across a ditch I did this but only to find myself separated from the fête by a lot of barbed wire and a wide vegetable garden; but at least I could see what was going on. Then I saw him! Jacko was standing just by the entrance to a large marquee, on the lawn, with crowds of people all around and someone making an announcement through the loudspeaker. Head feathers erect, he was strutting around and obviously enjoying himself no end. No one was taking any notice of the mischievous jackdaw and I realized that to them he was probably just some black-coloured bird that had alighted on the lawn.

'Jacko!' I hissed. 'Come *here*!' But he completely ignored me.

Feverishly I looked round for some way of getting into the large, rambling garden but there didn't seem to be one.

'Jacko!' I yelled again. 'Come HERE, you so-and-so!' But still he took no notice, though I'm sure he saw me. Instead, he wandered into the marquee, reappearing minutes later. At last a few people heard me, looking round and staring for the first time but I don't think they connected the red-faced demented lady in the floppy yellow hat madly waving her arms about with the bird on the lawn.

I was feeling hot, frustrated and furious with Jacko, who had now disappeared into the marquee again.

'Jacko – come back here!' I bellowed once again. I'd wring his neck when I caught him!

He reappeared again, stepping out jauntily on to the lawn. He was having a great time – all those lovely people and the noise and shouting and music! – and for the first time I realized that *this* was the sort of life he enjoyed, not the peace and quiet of the woods. Jacko was a towny, not a country bird.

Eventually the vicar cottoned on and tried to shoo this feathered member of his flock towards me but the jackdaw refused to co-operate and turned away to continue his strutting on the grass. The vicar gave up.

By now I was fuming. I came back through the hedge and ditch to the big field, once more walking alongside the fence. Hurrying through the swing gate at the top of the field, I turned right down the lane to the side entrance of the house where there was a huge wrought-iron gate; it looked like the entrance to Fort Knox. It was locked with a chain and hefty padlock – and there was no one in sight or calling distance, the fête taking place in a different part of the garden. While I was standing there wondering what to do next I heard an announcement that the fête was finishing and I became even more alarmed; what would my awful jackdaw do then? Would he go off with someone? . . . or fly through a window into the house and pinch the family jewels? . . . or peck one of the children? . . . I *had* to get him before he did something dreadful.

In the end I almost ran down the full length of the field and back to the house, pausing only for Eric – still sunning himself – to say, 'I *told* you! I knew this would happen,' as I flashed past. He was never one to mince words on these occasions. Jumping in the car I drove round and up another lane and steep hill to the front of the house; it was too far to walk when time was all important. Here I was at the entrance to the fête but now people were coming out, milling around and talking just inside the gate. There was no sign of Jacko. I hurried up to a young girl who was smiling and shaking hands with the middle-aged ladies departing; I guessed she was the daughter of the house.

'Er, I've just lost a jackdaw and I think he's in your garden somewhere. Would you mind if I looked?' It sounded a silly sort of thing to lose.

'Please do,' she answered, waving an arm in the general direction of the lawns.

I set off down a gravel path and across a lawn, searching everywhere and continually calling him. But still he didn't answer and I couldn't see the naughty jackdaw anywhere. I was beginning to despair.

'Have you tried up there?' The girl appeared from somewhere, pointing to the top of the garden which appeared to be raised above the main lawns and was hidden by shrubbery and hedges.

I turned and walked in the direction indicated. Hidden away up there was a swimming pool and there seemed to be some sort of private party in progress. Young people were swimming and diving and splashing about while others sat sipping drinks and watching. And right in the middle of all this was Jacko. He was standing on top of a small thatched roof over something – I forget exactly what it was but it was about the size of a roof you might find over a wishing-well – and he was being fed tit-bits. He was having another marvellous time and wasn't in the least pleased to see me.

Standing on a chair I just managed to reach him, Jacko somewhat reluctantly perching on my hand. Then I grabbed him . . . tight!

'He likes sausages,' one young man volunteered, looking at me curiously as I turned and stormed away. They all stared after me, looking sorry to see him go.

'I'll give you sausages!' I muttered as I shoved Jacko in his box on the car seat beside me. 'You *bad* boy!' I felt irritable, hot and utterly exhausted with the exertions of the past hour or two. And really angry with Jacko.

Jacko behaved himself better during the weeks that followed. I tried different tactics, taking him for a walk in the field early every evening and encouraging him to fly as much as possible. I figured that if he did more flying and got really tired he'd be less restless. And at first this seemed to work quite well. He flew from my shoulder all over the lower part of the field, seldom landing anywhere but twisting and turning in the air, swooping and diving – doing just about everything but loop the loop. Then, tired after his aerial display, he'd fly straight to me and land with the usual plop on my shoulder, hot and breathless, panting, his small eyes twinkling as much as to say, 'How am I doing?' A quick rest, then off again.

Sometimes when it was windy he'd battle against it and be blown all over the place. It was a joy to watch his skilful aerobatics; he was a marvellous flyer now and seemed to thoroughly enjoy demonstrating his skills. With feathers sleek with a blue-black sheen, he looked very different from the bedraggled bird he had been. I could hardly believe this was the bird with the frayed tail feathers that could only fly short distances.

Jacko was content just to perch on my shoulder, sometimes, as I walked round the field and occasionally he'd play with a tiny rubber ball I'd found, pouncing on it when it was thrown and then flying round the field with it in his beak before eventually dropping it somewhere. He did the same thing with other objects, such as a woolly glove, piece of stick or an old crow feather.

I enjoyed our evening walks and I'm certain Jacko did too. I hoped he'd forgotten the fête and his desire for a more social life. But, alas, he suddenly started leaving me from the other side of the field calling his 'Cheer-i-o!' and then flying off. 'Jacko . . . wait!' I'd shout at the retreating black figure, but next minute he'd disappeared from view, leaving me to walk home alone.

One night about 10.30 p.m. one of the tenants from a room further up the passage knocked on my door and asked if I knew that Jacko was in the River Bar of a local Thameside hotel? No, I didn't – and I wasn't at all pleased about it. Very tired and just getting ready for bed – Eric was already in his – I sighed deeply, put on a coat instead of my nightie and went out into the night to fetch him. He wasn't in the bar but the barman confirmed that the jackdaw had been there; he'd been in there before, apparently, and was in the habit of flying in and out through the open windows, he said. Did he behave himself, I dared to ask? Well, yes, on the whole. Though sometimes he'd been known to tweak a lady's earring or play with a measure or get up to other mischief round the tables, I was told. But he amused the customers and was very friendly with everyone. The barman himself did *not* sound very amused.

Having gleaned this information I gathered that Jacko was possibly in the foyer – he'd been seen heading that way – and that's where I found him. There was a dance on and a little group of people in evening dress had gathered out there; my awful jackdaw was on the shoulder of one of them, the centre of attention.

'Come on, you naughty boy!' I admonished, taking him on my hand.

'Oh . . . is he going? What a shame,' they all chorused, making me feel quite mean taking him away.

Walking the few hundred yards home in the dark I felt a bit of a Charlie with a jackdaw on my wrist, but I hadn't dared grab him in case he flew off.

Jacko went further and further afield after a few days at home, and for longer periods. I'd fitted out Stikki's old cage with everything I could possibly think of to please and amuse him – all kinds of toys and things – but it was no good; the urge to be off and away got the better of him each time. I used to worry a good deal about what mischief he might be getting up to, and one evening my worst fears looked like being realized. I got a phone call from Pam to ask if I could meet a lady on the common – four miles away – at a certain place because Jacko had pecked her little boy, drawn blood and had pulled out some of his hair.

'You'd better hurry,' Pam went on. 'It sounds bad. Jacko could be shot, you know, if the police get in on it.' With these comforting words she put down the receiver.

Horrified – the mother would surely murder me? – I abandoned the Sunday dinner I'd been cooking and dashed off in the car to the place mentioned where Jacko was apparently engaged in criminal activities. He'd been missing three weeks, this time, and this was the first report I'd had of him being seen. Often I received phone calls from all over the place.

When I reached the meeting place the only person to be seen was a young lad fishing for tiddlers in a stream under a small bridge on the edge of the common.

'Have you seen the boy who was attacked by a jackdaw?' I asked him, getting out of the car and walking over.

He looked up, grinning. 'Yes, it was me!'

'Oh. Er, are you all right? Did he hurt you?' I couldn't *see* any blood or hair missing.

'No. I'm okay. Just a scratch – here.' He indicated a tiny mark near one ear. 'I think it was 'cause I tried to catch 'im.'

I was relieved and also surprised; Pam had heard about it in a round-about sort of way and the report had obviously been grossly exaggerated somewhere along the line. The boy seemed fine and totally unconcerned about it all. His mother, when she appeared, was smiling and accepted my apologies and together they helped me look for Jacko. I gathered he'd been in the area for several days but, as usual, he'd now disappeared.

'I think he went over there,' said the boy, pointing across the wide expanse of common. I stared into the distance, shielding my eyes, and then I spotted him. Two people, mere specks on the horizon, had stopped walking and were twisting round, pointing and looking upwards; Jacko was the black dot circling and swooping overhead.

'Jack-ooo!' I yelled, cupping my hands and shouting several times as loudly as I could. He saw me and flew straight towards me, calling me as he flew. He landed on my shoulder, very breathless, and I ruffled his feathers as I carried him to the box in the car. It was a happy reunion . . .

'He's a beautiful bird, isn't he?' said the boy's mum as they both waved goodbye.

'I've got the potatoes on,' said Eric on our return. Then, later, 'That bird's a *menace*!' as he stabbed his finger at the subdued and tired figure of Jacko in his little box. He was even too tired to put up his shutter . . .

A week later Jacko was off again, missing for several days. This time he turned up in a kindergarten school a couple of miles away in the opposite direction.

'We've shut him in a cloakroom with one of the teachers,' the lady on the telephone said. 'Can you come and collect him?'

Heavens! Was he pulling out the teacher's hair now? I'd better hurry . . . anything might be happening!

But I needn't have worried – Jacko and the teacher seemed to have been getting on very well in the small cloakroom and I think she was quite sorry to see him go. So were the children when I carried him out through their classroom. 'Aah!' they all murmured, turning in their chairs to catch a glimpse of him. That was the trouble with my jackdaw; he won everyone's heart while leading me a merry dance. He could be a real charmer all right; but he could peck, too, if he happened to feel like it and I knew several people who were really frightened of him.

Another time when Jacko was gone for weeks I got a phone call from a pub five miles away.

'Er, the Red Lion here. We've got a jackdaw hanging around and I understand he might be yours?' the man said. He explained that the jackdaw had been there several times, wandering in and out of the pub and being fed tit-bits by the customers. 'He goes across the road when there's a wedding on at the church and mixes with the people there, too. He's quite a character, isn't he?'

I agreed he was indeed. 'Where is he now?' I asked.

'Well, I don't rightly know. He was here earlier but he seems to have gone just now.'

I sighed. The landlord promised to ring again if Jacko turned up. He didn't, at least, not then. Various other phone calls followed and reports that he'd been seen attending a local dance and had also been seen on a steamer trip down the river. 'He got off the boat at Boulter's Lock,' said this latter informant. 'But I don't know where he is now.' The same old story . . .

Jacko turned up, eventually, and stayed for a while. After each evening walk he returned home with me very soberly – no trouble at all, but I knew it wouldn't last and it didn't; off he went again.

This time Jacko took to going on pub crawls, visiting usually one of three local riverside hotels. First I rescued him from the bar of one, then from amidst people sitting at little tables on the lawn of another – and so on. Once when I was called out to fetch him from a terrace bar overlooking the river someone pointed to a full half-pint of beer on one of the tables. 'See that? That's Jacko's. The barman thought he might be thirsty, but he didn't like it.' Where was Jacko? Oh, he'd flown away a few minutes ago . . .

Well, at least my awful bird hadn't taken to drink. I cycled to the next hotel . . .

And so it went on. I had a box permanently strapped to my bicycle in case I met up with Jacko. It was too difficult to park the car on these short trips so I usually went by bike. Often, though, it was a wild goose chase and I returned home, hot and tired, without him.

On August Bank Holiday that year Jacko disappeared and I never saw him again. Enquiring in all the usual haunts drew a blank this time; no one had seen him around. Sadly I decided he must have been killed, perhaps on the road; once I'd found him strutting down the centre of one road with three motorbikes roaring away only inches from him, their young riders grinning as they watched the jackdaw. He seemed to have little respect for traffic.

Some weeks later, however, I heard of a jackdaw that had been hanging around a marina some miles up the river. Apparently this bird was very friendly and was enjoying rides on the boats, as well as being photographed with various children. It certainly sounded like my Jacko but when I rang the marina once again the bird had literally flown. No, they hadn't seen him for several days.

Then, about three months after his disappearance, I heard another rumour that a jackdaw had been seen near one of the locks in the opposite direction, but again it had disappeared.

It looked very much as if Jacko had settled for a life afloat . . .

I missed him, but it was obvious that he just wasn't the sort of bird you could keep caged for long and, love him as we did, he was a constant source of worry and anxiety. He was an incurable rascal, but a very charming and lovable one.

I hoped he'd manage to keep out of trouble and remain happy, wherever he was.

=12=

HORACE THE HERON

SOME time back I'd made another wooden cage slightly smaller than Clara's. It was on the floor, under my north window, and it housed a series of invalid sparrows that couldn't fly but liked to come out and hop around the room. The cage was fairly dark, missing the light and sun from the east window in the mornings but the sparrows liked it that way; dark corners to hide in suited them fine.

For some weeks a little posse headed by one-eyed Charlie, a cat victim, had hopped out each morning on my opening their door and scurried round the room. Sometimes they sunbathed in a patch of sunlight across the room, or bathed in a shallow dish of water, and on colder mornings they gathered in a semi-circle round the electric fire. After about half an hour or so they all trooped back and climbed into their cage. There was the occasional awkward one, of course, who hid under the bed and had to be chased, but for the most part they were very orderly and well behaved. I had cardboard tubes in the cage, about two inches in diameter and three or four inches long, some of them suspended by wire clips; sparrows love these and like to hide in them.

The morning hop-around was watched with great interest by Wol and Stikki – and Jacko, when he was at home. Of course they were never allowed out until all the sparrows were safely in again.

As well as Charlie there was Susie, lightly hit by a car but recovering; Jack, found injured in the busy High Street; Chester and Chan, two male car victims; and various others that came and went. Chester had an odd appearance. The knock from the car had somehow pushed his scalp to one side, making him look as if he were wearing a little tam-o'-shanter – one side of his head bunched with feathers and the other side pink and bare. He recovered and was free to leave but he remained with his sparrow friends in my room for several months, declining all offers of flight from an open window, before eventually flying away into the bushes.

I was very fond of my sparrows; none was the least bit like my little Chirpy but they were all dear little birds. Adult sparrows, I learned, were always very timid in captivity, preferring to hide away in the dark and to be handled as little as possible. The cage on the floor made this possible.

During the six months Jacko was with me I was brought 132 wild birds, all of which were housed and cared for by me in our two small rooms, Eric taking no part in the proceedings. Blackbirds (29), starlings (21) and sparrows (19) were by far the most numerous, but as well as these I treated the following: 10 pigeons, 8 housemartins, 7 song-thrushes, 4 moorhens, 4 dunnocks, 4 blue-tits, 4 robins, 3 woodpigeons, 3 swifts, 2 goldfinches, 2 swallows, 2 crows, 2 collared doves, 1 owl, 1 white dove, 1 coot, 1 goldcrest, 1 duckling, 1 pheasant, 1 chaffinch and 1 heron. Plus a budgie. The partridge in the pear-tree hadn't arrived yet! Of these, 76 died and 56 recovered. Remembering that many birds brought were often very badly injured, if not actually dying, and that no wild bird will allow itself to be picked up unless very sick indeed, this was quite a satisfactory average. Fifty-six lives saved, which is what it amounted to, made it all very worthwhile, I felt.

Besides all these birds there were the 'residents' to look after and feed, of course, like Wol, Stikki, Crusoe, and so on. It was very hard work and far from easy; sometimes I wished I had large aviaries and more space, like Pam. But I was managing . . . somehow.

I only put the 'overflow' into Eric's room when mine was really bursting at the seams mid-summer. He used to sit up in bed and try and identify the birds by the boxes they were in. 'What's that in Beefeater Gin? Oh, a sparrow. Well, which is the one in Snugglers? A blackbird . . .? Oh no . . . it's the moorhen, isn't it? The blackbird's in Smith's Crisps. And the two blue-tits in Fairy Liquid? Got it!' And so on.

Horace the heron was my largest and most difficult patient during this period. It happened in this way.

One afternoon a gentleman who lived in the country 'miles from anywhere' rang me; could I possibly collect a very sick heron?

'Two schoolboys found him – we've got him in a tea-chest.'

'Does he appear to be injured?' I asked.

'Well, not as far as we can see. We don't really know what's wrong. He looks very ill.'

'I'll be right over,' I said weakly, writing down the instructions on how to get there. His bungalow was some miles away down endless winding lanes. I knew I'd get lost – I always did in that area, my sense of direction being practically non-existent. After I'd walked back to my room from the telephone it suddenly hit me: a *heron*? Where on earth was I going to put such a large bird? I had no room at all.

I drove off, a large empty box in which I put thick layers of newspaper and hay on the back seat, and the directions on a piece of paper beside me. After several wrong turnings I was lost, all right, and I ended up in the drive of a golf clubhouse. There had been no sign of the wrought-iron gates I was supposed to be looking out for. When someone says, 'You can't miss it,' why *do* I always?

The only two men in the clubhouse looked at me indifferently and went on with their conversation, one merely waving a languid hand towards the telephone in a small office. They said they'd never heard of the place I wanted. They weren't very helpful at all, but they accepted the ten pence offered for thirty seconds on the telephone.

After further directions I arrived at my destination and there was the heron in the tea-chest outside the front door. He was lying very still with closed eyes, his long bill resting on the bottom of the box. He certainly didn't look too good. He was also very wet, his grey feathers soaked, as he'd been found in the middle of a field during the wet spell of weather we'd been having. I couldn't see any injury, however.

'I can't get the tea-chest in the car – I'll have to lift him into the box,' I told the man, lifting the bird rather gingerly. He seemed all legs and neck.

So ill did he look I half expected the heron to be dead before I got him home and I only hoped I wouldn't run out of petrol or get lost on the way back. Happily, Horace, as I called him, was still alive when I arrived without further incident, and I quickly put hot-water bottles each side of him to hot him up; his body felt very cold. On further examination I still couldn't find anything physically wrong with the bird, though, and I was puzzled. What was up with him? He was young, not fully matured; was there a clue there somewhere?

I made up some Farex baby food, which I used for most sick or immature birds, and squirted some down Horace's throat, repeating this every hour. He offered no resistance when I forcibly opened his beak, being too weak to protest or even be afraid. He was rather difficult to feed, as his beak was so long and narrow that the milk food was inclined to dribble out the other side instead of going down his throat, but I persevered and managed to get him to swallow most of it.

The box was still standing in the middle of my room; where *could* I put it? It looked as if it would have to go in Eric's room; maybe on top of the old trunk in the corner? I staggered in there with Horace. Later, Eric dashed in for a cup of tea but he didn't notice the new box with the heron. I decided I'd tell him about it later.

When he'd gone I rang Pam for some information about herons; I'd never had one before but I knew she had.

'They can make a terrible noise, you know,' she warned me after we'd chatted for a few minutes. 'It sounds like tin plates dropping on concrete. Very loud.'

'Charming. I hope he doesn't do it in the night. I've put him in Eric's room.'

She gave a hollow laugh. 'The best of luck – sounds like you may need it! 'Bye now.'

Meanwhile Horace was drying out nicely and by mid-evening he stood up for the first time, his yellow eyes opening and his snake-like neck relaxed on his back in the normal posture. I was delighted! He stared at me balefully as I advanced with the syringeful of Farex once more. The food seemed to have worked wonders and he appeared to be getting stronger all the time. By late evening I could hardly believe it was the same bird. And I thought I knew now what had been the matter with him: quite simply, the heron had been slowly dying of hunger. Mother herons are inclined to be neglectful and probably young Horace had never learned to catch food and fend for himself. So he'd just been crouching in the wet field getting weaker and weaker and would soon have died of starvation if the two boys hadn't found him. What he needed now was plenty of food.

Eric came in again later and this time he saw Horace all right.

'What's *that?*' he exclaimed, stopping short and staring as he entered the room.

'That's Horace – he's a heron.'

'A *heron?* We can't have a heron in here!' He looked at me, aghast, as he flung his coat on the bed.

'Well, we've got one.' I explained what had happened.

Eric frowned. I could see that he wasn't keen on a heron as a room-mate.

'Can't he go in your room?'

'There just isn't any room . . . where could I possibly put him?'

'That's your worry.'

I sighed. My husband could be very unreasonable at times. I mean, I wasn't asking him to sleep with a tiger . . . just a little heron. He didn't even know about the possibility of a tin-plate-on-concrete noise in the night yet either.

I carried Horace back into my room just before we went to bed. Better, I decided, than a summons to remove him in the wee small hours. Supposing he *did* make that noise? Eric would go mad!

But I had another problem staring me in the face; standing up, Horace was too tall for the box – I couldn't cover it or stop him jumping out, if he wanted to. When he extended his neck his head was higher than the top of the box. I had had to put one armchair on top of the other to squeeze his box in by the door as it was, but how could I solve this latest problem?

In the end I went outside with a torch and found some wire-netting which I fixed over the heron's box like a kind of dome. Then I covered him up for the night with an old curtain. At least now he would be able to stand up all night if he wished. It was only temporary, of course; in the morning I'd have to think of something else, perhaps find an even larger box somewhere?

Wol, needless to say, had been watching all this activity with the usual great interest from his high perch, and now I slipped him into the cage with the already sleeping Stikki and that was the last bird covered for the night. I climbed wearily into bed.

'Aaark, Aaark!' The truly ear-splitting cry rent the stillness of the night air waking me with such a jump I nearly hit the ceiling. Pam wasn't exaggerating! I looked at my watch: 4.20 a.m. I'd been deeply asleep and it took me a few seconds to gather my thoughts. Firstly, I thought what a good thing it was I hadn't left Horace in Eric's room. Secondly, I thought the heron must be feeling a good deal better to make a noise like *that* in the middle of the night. I got out of bed and peeped under his cover. He was standing up in the relaxed position. He looked fine. Smiling, I slid back into bed.

In the morning I carried Horace back into Eric's room again . . . after he'd gone to work. I acquired a larger, deeper box which, with the flaps extended upwards, proved to be just tall enough to house the heron and allow a half-cardboard and half-Twilweld cover over the top. It was no good, there just *wasn't* permanent space in my room. I was a little worried about what Eric would say, though. And supposing Horace made that noise again? I didn't intend to tell him about that – I would just keep my fingers crossed and hope for the best.

Later that morning Eric went to buy Horace some sprats but returned saying that they were out of season and he'd had to buy the more expensive whitebait instead. Horace wolfed down the whitebait in no time at all, snatching them from my fingers and gulping them always headfirst. It looked as if he were going to cost me a fortune! But I was pleased to see him eating so well and beginning to look fit and well again. I was quite certain now that it was lack of food that had caused his weakness – he'd made such a quick and remarkable recovery.

For two days Horace ate whitebait and then happily Eric discovered a shop that sold large sardines the size of small herrings in frozen blocks. These worked out a lot cheaper, though still expensive when Horace had had his fill. The young heron now had an insatiable appetite and it looked like costing me £1 a day just to feed him. I was certainly glad I hadn't got several heron patients! In the end I just had to ration him to about half a pound of fish a day, always leaving a bowl of soaked Go-Cat dried cat food – very popular with many birds – for in-between snacks.

Of course all this fish had a rather alarming side effect. I was in Eric's room when the latter came home, tired and rather niggly.

'Pheew! What a terrible smell!'

'Oh, hello, darling. I've just made some tea. I'll pour you ou—'

'Fish . . . that's what it is! Pheeew . . . what a *stink*!'

He went over and glared at Horace. 'What's *he* doing back in here again anyway? I thought he was staying in your room?'

I explained. Then, suddenly, the worst happened.

'Poooh! What a *stench*!'

Well, what goes in has to come out and Horace had just made one of his stinky, fishy messes. It was unfortunate, just when Eric was standing there.

'All right, all right – I was just going to clean him out. It'll be okay when I've sloshed lots of disinfectant around – you'll see,' I reassured him.

For about the tenth time that day I removed all Horace's bedding and cleaned him out but it took about half a bottle of disinfectant and four cups of tea for Eric before he was placated . . .

And so it was each day. Horace got stronger and stronger while I got weaker and weaker, with all that scrubbing out! When I cleaned the box I usually had to remove Horace. This wasn't easy; his neck was so sinuous and snaky and I had to watch my eyes with that dagger-like beak. Then there were the long legs to contend with – what knobbly knees he had! – and sometimes I felt like Alice in Wonderland playing croquet with a flamingo tucked under one arm as a mallet.

Eric was very good about getting the sardines, though, and came in again and again with yet another frozen block. We had the small fridge but no freezer so I couldn't stock up with them, and the only shop that sold these large sardines was way out of town. I was grateful for his help.

Horace was with me just two weeks – it felt like two years – and then he went to be rehabilitated and taught to fish in a special bird sanctuary with a large pond. After two months he was able to be released in a local heronry; by that time he was flying well and catching fish for himself.

When he left me the first thing I did was carry his old box outside and burn it. After gallons of disinfectant it still smelled of fish and had got thoroughly soggy.

I was glad to have helped Horace but I was even more glad I didn't have herons brought in every day.

═13═

THE PIGEON
ON THE WARDROBE

THAT winter we had a spot of bother with a pigeon. One cold day Eric came home with a feral pigeon – the sort you see on ledges and rooftops in any town. Pidge, as we unimaginatively called her – it turned out to be female – was found strolling round the garage showroom among the then new Ford Fiesta cars that were being launched that very morning. The management weren't very pleased; they didn't take kindly to pigeon droppings on their highly polished floor and they were waiting for important people in the motor industry for the celebration. Pidge was shooed outside. But she continued to hang around, looking rather dazed and lost, so she was caught, bundled into a box and brought to me.

I examined her but found nothing wrong, so I put her in a large box with food, water and a perch and left her to it. She passed the day alternately eating and sleeping; trying to sell the Ford Fiesta seemed to have taken a lot out of her . . .

Next morning I released Pidge from my window. She spent two hours on the roof surveying the landscape and then flew away; that was that I thought – in my extreme naïvety; she's probably gone back to wherever she came from originally. I knew very little about pigeons in those days.

She was back, of course, next morning, tucking into crumbs on my window sill, much to the annoyance of the small birds who were my regular customers on cold winter days. After eating she flew up into the elm tree opposite my side window, spending the day perching in the tree and eating on the sill; same as she'd done in the box the previous day. Pidge didn't look as if she'd the slightest intention of going anywhere else at all . . . ever.

73

For my part I had not yet learned the golden rule: never start feeding a pigeon unless you want it for keeps. Pidge hung around like this for several days, then, one morning, I found her balanced on top of the tall window in Eric's room, the sash slightly open. After a while she flew off but returned later to roost there for the night, crouching down with her tail sticking into the room. Next morning I opened the window a little wider; if she must sleep up there it would give her more room, I thought, being a soft-hearted fool.

I was very busy during the day and forgot all about Pidge, but early evening I glanced up at Eric's window and saw that she wasn't there. Had she flown away at last? No, she hadn't. Pidge had taken the more widely opened window as an invitation to enter the room, apparently, and she was now standing on one leg, fast asleep, on some boxes on top of the large old-fashioned mahogany wardrobe.

Eric came home and started telling me about the day's events as he changed his clothes.

'Ssh' I said, finger to lips. 'You'll wake her.' Tongue in cheek, I wanted to see what he'd say.

'Uh? Wake who?' he asked, looking round suspiciously.

'Pidge. She's up there.' I pointed to the wardrobe.

He wasn't too happy about it, but maybe it was better than a heron?

'Well, I hope she's not going to start cooing or anything in the night. What about the mess?'

'I've put some newspaper down up there. I don't think she'll disturb you.'

'She'd better not!'

But she did; early morning when it grew light Pidge wanted to go out and she flew across the room to the window, scrabbling against the drawn yellow curtains. Eric had to get out of bed and let her out; *not* very popular.

We both got very fond of our resident pigeon, however, and she made Eric's wardrobe her headquarters from then on, roosting there every night and always taking a nap up there in the afternoons. She also came in if it was very cold or rainy, in fact she was in and out all day.

Pidge seemed particularly fond of Eric; he used to stand facing her, chatting away, and she'd puff herself out and strut around cooing back at him, 'Ouooooo!' on a rising note, her head bobbing.

She was with us nearly four months. When spring came she became more and more ardent in her courtship of Eric and we decided it was time she found a mate. We took her to Pam's aviary and released her in there with the many other pigeons. Almost before you could say knife Pidge had mated with a handsome young male bird and later we heard they'd nested, laid two eggs and successfully reared the two youngsters.

Our Pidge was a mum!

I had another pigeon during this period but this time it was an injured one; a white pigeon called Snowy. One afternoon there was a knock on the door and a man outside holding the usual large cardboard-box. Quickly he thrust it into my hands. 'Here you are,' he said, immediately turning and walking away down the passage before I could say a word.

'Hey – just a minute!' I called after him. 'What is it and where did you find it?' I liked to find out as much as I could about a new patient. It sometimes helped.

'Found it at work,' said this chap gruffly. He seemed to be a man of few words. He'd stopped and taken a few paces back towards me but now he turned and made off again.

'Where do you work?' I persisted. 'Do you know what's wrong with the bird . . . what *is* it?' I wished he'd stay still a couple of minutes so we could discuss the matter.

'Pigeon,' he grunted, shuffling back to my door. 'It'll be all right. Got an 'ole in it, but it'll be all right.' By now he was halfway down the passage again but he paused and looked back. 'Got an 'ole in it,' he repeated. 'Found it in the yard, peckin' around, so it's all right.' He disappeared quickly after this long sentence.

Gingerly I opened the flaps of the box. I failed to see how any bird with a hole in it could be entirely all right. What sort of a hole? It didn't sound at all all right.

Inside the box was a very dirty and bedraggled white pigeon – at least, it must have been white once. Now it was more of a very dirty grey. It had indeed got a hole in it – the bird's crop had split open revealing a round, gaping hole about the size of a golf ball. Encrusted round the edges were what looked like dirty yellow lumps of cheese which I took to be partly digested food.

Snowy seemed surprisingly perky and untroubled by this rather nasty looking injury – less so than I was. Would food go into his stomach if I fed him, I wondered, or would it come out again through the hole? I rang up three people who I thought might know the answer but they were all a bit vague; no one was sure. So I cleaned up the crop the best I could, dusting it liberally with Sulphanilamide powder, an antibiotic very useful for bird injuries, and then fed him Farex, watching to see if it came through the hole. It didn't. So I continued to feed him this at regular intervals, also bread-and-milk occasionally.

Nine days later Snowy's crop had almost healed. Gradually the hole had grown smaller, finally disappearing beneath the thick white breast feathers. He started preening and became really snowy white again, and he was picking up corn nicely now.

Seventeen days after he came the pigeon was able to fly away from my window. Pure white and positively dazzling in the winter sunshine he was a most pretty bird. I wished 'Mr Gotanole' had been around to witness the departure.

=14=

MAGPIE CAPERS

BUZBY was a magpie, another winter patient. He'd been shot and had a nasty wound in his upper side, almost under one wing, and a broken leg the other side. He'd been found in a field. Gunshot wounds both saddened and angered me; if people must shoot birds – and magpies and pigeons were not protected by law – then why couldn't they shoot to kill instead of leaving the poor things to die slowly of injuries or starvation in a field?

I took Buzby to the vet, who strapped up his broken leg and treated the wound. Back home, when he'd recovered a little, I tried to persuade the magpie to eat but he was an awkward customer and seemed to dislike everything offered. Magpies eat almost anything, said my bird book, but this one didn't. He refused cereal, cake, raw mince, bread-and-milk, tinned dog and cat food, biscuits, sultanas, and egg of any kind, toying only with small pieces of apple and crumbled Digestive biscuit; he ate the latter very half-heartedly in an all-right-if-you-insist sort of way, though.

I'd put him in a strong rectangular box underneath my north window, on top of the sparrow cage. The box was open at the top and almost level with the bottom of the window, so I covered it with the usual half-cardboard and half-Twilweld, the latter folding back to allow access to the box or fastening down with the usual paper-clip hook I always made. After two weeks the leg had mended and I was able to take the strapping off. He'd been standing on a thick perch on the one good leg most of the time, but now he started putting a little weight on the other leg as it gradually grew stronger. The wound was healing nicely, too, but there was bad news; the shot had damaged the wing muscle and he would never fly again.

Buzby had finally settled on a diet of Whiskas Supermeat with Rabbit. It had to be 'with rabbit' – with anything else and he wouldn't eat it. One day, for a change, I offered him a very large long worm, dangling it in front of his beak. He didn't seem very interested so I placed it on the soil floor of his box and went away. He was a very furtive eater and would never touch a thing if I was watching him or even in the room at all.

When I returned about ten minutes later he was sitting smugly on his perch blinking at me – like Wol, he blinked rapidly when nervous – and there scattered all over the floor of the box were horrible mangled-looking pieces of pink worm. He'd killed the thing but apparently decided against actually eating it; Whiskas Supermeat was better! I still shudder at the thought of the multiple pieces of squashy fat worm that I had to sort out and remove; some of them were still wriggling in the nasty way bits of worm have. Ugh!

Buzby was getting very restless and I worried about what to do with him; he was too big a bird to keep permanently in my already over-crowded room. Besides, nearly all other birds have an instinctive fear of magpies and when he made his cackling noise it upset my other smaller inmates. For the same reason Pam couldn't have him in one of her aviaries. I would have to find a home for him somewhere. Being unable to fly he obviously could never be released.

Christmas came and went. Some weeks before I'd photographed Wol with a little Father Christmas hat on his head and sprigs of holly each side of him, turning him into a Christmas card. He hadn't minded this at all and the cards were much appreciated by our friends and relatives.

Buzby decided to celebrate New Year's Day by leaping out of the window. Carelessly I'd omitted to close the one over his box before opening the wire flap and, taking fright as I replaced a water-pot, he sprang out into the garden and quickly disappeared into the shrubbery with great leaps and much cackling.

Dashing outside, I gave chase but the magpie had vanished into some thick undergrowth, making for the fields bordering the garden and by the time I'd squeezed through some barbed wire and negotiated a muddy ditch he was nowhere to be seen. I should explain here that at the bottom of the big field between us and the woods and lake there was a smaller field, and dividing the two was a wide ditch with trees and bushes each side meeting overhead and forming a kind of tunnel. There was also a wide, tangled mass of blackberry bushes, old but dense and strongly growing, and these brambles formed a veritable jungle, along with all the other undergrowth, and were at least eight feet high in places.

I decided that Buzby must have gone into this tangled, prickly thicket.

I stopped and listened, hoping to hear the familiar magpie cackle, but he remained silent; where *was* he? Eric came and joined me and together we searched for a good half hour. 'He's gone . . . you'll never find him in this!' exclaimed my husband in his usual pessimistic way. 'If this is what he wants, leave him!' He stormed off, cursing Buzby, and left me to it.

Of course I couldn't possibly leave him – I just had to find that bird somehow or he'd certainly die. The half-wild cats or a fox would surely get him in the night, since he couldn't fly, if he remained on the ground. I was cold and wet and very muddy but I kept on searching. After an hour, though, with still no sign of the elusive magpie, I was beginning to despair. 'You stupid bird – where *are* you?' I yelled into the thicket. I, too, was cursing him now, temper getting the better of me in my anxiety and frustration.

Just then I caught sight of a man walking his dog across the field; it was a favourite haunt for dog owners. I had an idea and called the man who came towards me, a golden spaniel bounding beside him.

'Er, is your dog any good at finding things?' I asked hopefully, bending down and patting the animal.

'Depends,' he answered, smiling. 'What've you lost?'

'A magpie,' I said, feeling a bit silly. I explained.

'Hmm, I see. Well let's see if Sam can flush him out.' Then 'Go on, Sam!' he encouraged, seconds later. 'Go on!'

With wagging tail the spaniel plunged into the dense brambles and a few moments later Buzby appeared, floundering about high up on the top and in the very middle of the huge bush; Sam had flushed him out all right but the magpie had somehow sprung upwards instead of emerging into the field. We couldn't possibly reach him.

For the next half hour the same thing kept happening. Sam disturbed the magpie who scrambled high into the top of the blackberry bushes; Sam then came out and Buzby promptly jumped down on to the ground in the very centre of the thicket. Over and over again this happened in a most frustrating manner. Try as we both did – our clothes in danger of being torn to shreds – we just couldn't get him.

Sam the spaniel thought it a great game. A young dog, he was having a marvellous time. He kept reappearing from the dark depths of the bushes, pink tongue lolling out and pieces of blackberry bush sticking to his feathery ears and coat as he wagged his tail and panted, grinning up at his master. But we were getting nowhere fast. The man glanced at his watch. 'Er, I really think I'll have to be going now,' he said. 'I'm sorry about your magpie. Perhaps if you leave him a while he'll come out into the field eventually? It might be worth a try.'

I thanked him profusely for his kindness, patted the dog and we parted.

Back indoors I kept pacing around and staring out of the window, unable to relax. Soon it would be getting dark and then what? I was very worried about Buzby. Apart from anything else I'd grown fond of him. As the evening shadows lengthened some time later I told Eric I was going out to have another look; maybe the magpie had come out?

'You're wasting your time,' said my husband, encouraging as ever.

Buzby hadn't emerged – there was no sign of him still. I dived desperately into the outer layers of bramble, penetrating as far as I could and peering into the darkness; no magpie. Perhaps he had moved nearer the house? There were a lot more blackberry bushes in that vicinity, even more tangled and impenetrable. Throwing caution to the wind I dived into these next and was virtually on my knees crawling about in the thorny undergrowth when I heard a shout from the house.

'Come quickly! Come quickly!' Eric was yelling, then, seconds later, 'Hurry up!' – impatiently this time.

He's got to be joking, I thought, as I backed out slowly and carefully, the vicious thorns clinging to my person as if reluctant to give me up. Hurrying was impossible. Staggering and stumbling back through the assault course to our garden – I had to get caught up in the barbed wire in my hurry, didn't I? – I was spurred on by another shout from Eric. As I ran up I saw him standing outside near the window of his room facing the overgrown flower-bed opposite.

'Buzby's in there!' he yelled. 'Look!'

And there he was, only about twenty yards from where I'd been searching.

Eric explained that he'd been reading the paper indoors when he'd heard the raucous cackling of a magpie. Jumping up he'd looked out of the window just in time to see a big black cat spring on Buzby. Apparently as it sprang he leaped to one side, and this was repeated three or four times.

'Each time the cat pounced Buzby neatly side-stepped,' Eric said.

'Didn't you *do* something?' I asked. Surely he hadn't just stood and watched this drama.

'Of course – I banged on the window and yelled. Then I went

outside and shooed it away.' He said the cat had slunk away into the bushes; no doubt it was disappointed that magpie wasn't to be on the menu that night.

As I came on the scene Buzby, awkward as ever, leaped under another barbed-wire fence – it was like Colditz round our garden – and back into the field beyond the flower-bed, promptly disappearing in a tunnel of long, overgrown couch-grass. I gave chase, determined not to lose him again and eventually caught him in a flying tackle any Rugby player would have been proud of, ending up lying full length on my stomach in the wet grass, my outstretched hands just managing to clutch the bird. My feelings as I stood up, Buzby firmly gripped in my hands, were mixed; I didn't know whether to kiss him or kill him!

The magpie was none the worse for this adventure, eating his supper and settling down on his perch in the box for the night. As for me, I was exhausted, and I spent a good twenty minutes cleaning up, picking bits of bramble out of my hair and clothing and pulling painful thorns from my fingers, arms and legs.

'The things you do for your birds!' exclaimed Kay on hearing about all this. 'Honestly, Joan! *I* don't know.' She shook her neatly coiffeured head in disbelief.

Mine always looked as if I'd come through a hedge backwards. Often I *had*.

Four weeks later Buzby went to a good home with some kind people who loved birds. They'd made him a special enclosure and little magpie house down the garden, and I drove him there and saw him safely installed. There were hens and a duck strolling free in the garden so he'd have company. 'Don't worry – we'll look after him,' said this chap with a parrot on his shoulder as he said goodbye.

I felt confident they would.

=15=

GOOSE ON THE LAWN

ONE busy Saturday morning the telephone rang; could I come and rescue a goose that was sitting on this gentleman's lawn?

'A goose?' I queried. 'What seems to be the matter with it?' I hadn't had a goose before – whatever was I going to do with *that*?

'It's a Canada goose,' the man said. 'It's been shot. In two places, we think.'

'I'll come along,' I said, jotting down his address.

I prepared the largest box I could find and Eric drove me round to the house about half a mile away.

'Are you coming to help catch him?' I asked hopefully as I climbed out of the car.

'No bloody fear!' he exclaimed emphatically as he shook up his newspaper. 'I'll wait here.'

The gentleman took me round to the back of the house where there was a long stretch of garden and there, sure enough, was a large goose, black neck outstretched and head turned towards us. He was lying in the middle of the lawn down the far end. It looked as if it might have been easy, picking up an injured goose, but it wasn't; it took five of us about half an hour to catch him. He looked docile enough lying nonchalantly on the grass but each time we closed in on him the big goose waddled away and somehow managed to give us the slip. Once he tried to fly but crash-landed into some shrubbery. He was surprisingly agile in spite of his injuries.

'Have you got a large rug or blanket?' I asked. 'Something we could throw over him?'

Someone found an old blanket and eventually I managed to grab the goose by his long neck, yelling for somebody to catch hold of his body, and at last we heaved him into the box, blanket and all. It was a tight fit; the box was only just big enough. We were all fairly exhausted; he was a very strong and awkward bird and I was certainly glad I'd had four helpers. Eric drove me straight to our local vet but as the latter was out we had to leave the goose, and I arranged to pick him up later.

'Do you want me to come with you?' Eric asked when the time came to collect him.

'No, I can manage. It's all right,' I said. I knew he didn't really want another drive to the vet. It was almost opening time.

I returned alone to collect Honky, as I'd christened him. It was dark when I pulled into the small car park of the surgery which was down a quiet side road; no one else was around and mine was the only car. The goose had been given an antibiotic injection and his wounds inspected, the girl who opened the door said. It was decided not to upset the bird further by probing for shots so he was ready to be taken away. She handed the goose over, said goodnight and locked the door, turning out the lights. There were no other patients that Saturday evening.

I carried Honky in his large box to the car and it was then my troubles began. He was very heavy and I could only just manage to carry him on my own. My problem now was that I couldn't get the door of our old Ford Cortina to stay open long enough to lift the box on to the rear seat. It was too large to go in the boot or on the front passenger seat. It was a two-door saloon and the door just refused to stay open – to add to my troubles the tipped-forward driver's seat kept falling back, too, as I struggled and struggled with the cumbersome box. I definitely needed two, if not three pairs of hands and there wasn't a soul in sight to help. To make matters even worse the interior light of the car wasn't working.

After a good twenty minutes I managed at last to heave the goose into the car by keeping the door open with one foot and the seat forward with my knee, scraping my shins badly in the process. Why had I told Eric I could manage? If ever I'd needed his help it was now. I drove home.

'Ah . . . You've got him?' said Eric cheerfully on my return. He was just going out. 'You've managed all right, then?'

He helped me lift Honky into the previously prepared big hutch – the one the eight ducklings slept in – in the shed. I'd decided the goose would have to go in there; there wasn't really anywhere else I could possibly put him. It was very dark in the shed but Eric had fixed up a small battery-operated light in one corner of the hutch and we switched this on. The shed had no light. Then I examined the first Canada goose patient I'd ever had.

Honky had been shot twice, one shot having entered his cheek, missing his eye by less than two inches, and the second had entered his flank the opposite side. His eye was badly swollen and closed and both wounds were still bleeding, staining his white feathers. But he didn't seem too unhappy, in fact he looked quite perky.

I bathed his eye in a weak saline solution and put a little Terramycin ointment in, then I fed him some bread-and-milk and afterwards left him for the night. He needed a good rest, now. Just as I was about to leave the shed, however, the goose suddenly rose to his feet, arched his huge wings and hissed loudly in my ear making me jump. It was a very loud and fierce-sounding hiss and totally unexpected – he'd seemed so placid.

For the next few days I fed Honky by hand every few hours, forcing open his strong beak and popping in bread-and-milk. He wouldn't pick up food for himself. It wasn't easy as he kept his beak clenched tight and his sinewy neck twisted away; again I wished I'd got two pairs of hands! His eye was treated every day, too, and gradually the swelling went down and the eye opened. Fortunately his sight seemed unimpaired. His wounds were healing slowly, too. He always hissed at me when I entered the shed each morning, sounding like some giant cobra lurking at the back. It was always dark in there as there was no window and the hutch, of course, was right across the back. But he soon calmed down when I fondled his neck and spoke soothingly to him and he got quite tame after a while, laying his neck on my arm while I did his eye. Canada geese have very beautiful eyes – large, for the size of the head, and dark and liquid.

One evening a girl who was in the habit of leaving her moped near the entrance of the shed told me an amusing story. She'd returned home from work in the dark and leaned her bike against the shed as usual. She was just walking away when she heard a loud hissing noise, so she turned back and examined her tyres, thinking she'd got a puncture. Then she realized the noise was coming from the shed.

'I'd no idea you'd got a goose in there,' she laughed.

On the fifth day Honky was so much better that I lifted him out of the hutch for a waddle round the shed. I wasn't sure whether he was strong enough to be released yet or not; I wanted to see how he'd get on. Fixing what I thought was an adequate wire-netting frame barrier across the open doorway I went indoors to prepare lunch.

An hour later I returned. Honky appeared to have been trying to decorate the shed with bread-and-milk – it was everywhere! He'd at last started feeding himself so I hoped he'd at least swallowed some of it. I'd tried him with various other food, but bread-and-milk was his favourite; he loved it. He was waddling around and pecking at things and seemed quite happy, so I left him and went indoors again.

When I came out half an hour later the Canada goose had gone. To my dismay I found the wire frame had fallen down and the bird had literally flown. There was no sign of him in the garden or anywhere around, though I searched everywhere.

I rang the police in case he'd flopped down in someone else's garden again.

'No, madam,' the sergeant said. 'No goose on our books, I'm afraid.' He paused. 'We've one bird – a three inch little white bird with a red beak that someone's found, but no goose.'

I tried the RSPCA. They promised to let me know if they heard of an injured Canada goose being found. Evening came and still no news of Honky. I consoled myself by thinking that perhaps this was a good sign; it must surely mean he'd flown right away and perhaps joined other geese up the river? There were plenty around. I hoped so.

=16=

AN EXPLOSION OF ROBINS

SPRING came at last and the baby birds and fledglings started to come in. They were hard work, tiny ones having to be fed every twenty minutes or so all day long and fledglings every hour or two, but I loved them all and looked forward to this time of year. It was a tie, though, and when I went shopping I had to rush up to the town and back in between feeds in double-quick time. Sometimes Eric fetched me things, including the large frozen lump of ox heart I bought each week for Wol and Stikki. This I then meticulously cut into daily portions, carefully removing all fat and gristle. This latter was thrown outside for the tits and other less fussy birds. Crusoe liked 'ox heart day' as he always got a few pieces as a treat. He used to watch me cutting it up on the table, fidgeting and making crow noises in eager anticipation. The slices of frozen ox heart were then stored in the freezer compartment of the fridge, one piece being got out every evening for the next day's ration and allowed to defrost during the night. Stikki, in particular, was extremely fussy about his meat being absolutely fresh. I had to be very firm with the butcher about not selling me limp ox heart during the hot weather as they simply wouldn't eat it. It wasn't any good him assuring me it was perfectly fresh and 'Fit for human consumption, madam,' if Wol and Stikki didn't think it was fit for owl and kestrel consumption!

'They're *spoilt*! – that's what's the matter,' said Eric. 'It's ridiculous!'

I suppose he was quite right but I always liked to give my birds the best I could.

One afternoon a lady rang me up and asked if I could take a nest of baby robins. She said they had been deserted by their parents.

'Are you quite sure they've been deserted?' I asked as I always did. Many so called 'deserted' nests weren't so at all. As often as not the parent birds were merely keeping out of the way, watchful and waiting, until the person disturbing or near their nest had gone away. Certain they weren't being watched, the parent birds then returned to their brood and commenced feeding again, often very secretly.

'Yes, absolutely certain,' she insisted. '*Quite* sure.' She went on to explain that the nest had been disturbed during gardening activities and afterwards a watch had been kept on it 'for several days', but there had been no sign at all of the baby birds being fed. I was more than ever convinced now that it had *not* been deserted; if the young robins hadn't been fed for several days they'd surely be dead by now?

Before I could suggest this, however, the lady said, 'I've managed to get what's left of the nest into a box. I'll bring it round.'

Half an hour later I was handed five small robin fledglings in part of a rather dilapidated nest.

'I hope they'll be all right,' the lady murmured anxiously before she left. 'They may not have been fed for several days.'

Shortly after their arrival each of the baby robins passed a dropping in one of the neat little bags that Nature provides. The lady had told me she hadn't given them anything, so this meant they definitely *had* been fed by their parents . . . and fairly recently.

I felt rather sad about the whole thing, but the lady meant well and now it was up to me to try and rear the youngsters. Perhaps the parent birds would find consolation in a second brood later.

They were charming little brown speckled birds, round as balls and almost fully fledged, with baby down still sticking to parts of their bodies. They all looked healthy enough; certainly not neglected.

I'd reinforced the remains of the nest with soft hay, keeping the moss, hair and wool lining the cup just as it was in the centre and placing the whole thing in a larger box with my old Tin Lizzie hot-water bottle encased in the usual woolly sock for warmth and comfort. They'd opened their tiny beaks, squeaking for food, so I popped in morsels of raw mince. After two bits each they shut their beaks, firmly closed their eyes and snoozed.

During the next few days I was kept frantically busy feeding the family from six o'clock in the morning until eight at night. They yelled the place down with shrill, distraught cries if kept waiting longer than twenty minutes, and I began to have greater admiration for parent birds than ever before; how on earth did they keep up the pace?

I had other youngsters to feed, too, including several blackbirds, three starlings and a thrush. Young blackbirds were being brought in almost daily. And then of course there were my 'residents'. When I wasn't feeding I was usually cleaning up after the youngsters – the droppings had to be removed after each feed in order to keep the boxes reasonably clean and I kept tissues in a corner of each box for this purpose. Then there was Eric, meals, housework, etc., each day; spring was a hectic time.

After five days of feeding the robin fledglings I felt quite whacked. It seemed I'd no sooner fed the little birds than they were hungry again, dancing around with tiny fluttery wings and clamouring for more . . . more . . . MORE!

One of the five kept spitting out mince, though the others loved it, so I fed it mainly Farex, which they were mad on and had several times a day. I tried them on chopped worms, on one occasion.

'How about chopping up those little worms for me, darling?' I asked Eric one day, tongue in cheek and indicating the chopping block.

'What!' He was aghast, taking me seriously. 'You chop your own blankety-blank worms!' He left the room hurriedly.

The robins didn't like the chopped worms, making a lot of fuss and refusing to swallow any. They made it quite clear they preferred raw mince; memories of Kweekie.

After the first two days I'd put the robins in the budgie cage and in between eating they perched in a row on the old Tin Lizzie in its sock, loving the warmth. Occasionally they perched on one of the twiggy perches or nestled in the blue woolly hat, which they also loved. It was easier to feed them in this cage. I used to open the door and allow one robin to hop out, closing the door again quickly. Then I fed the robin that had jumped out and popped it back in the cage, calling, 'Next!' whereupon a second robin hopped out and the process was repeated. This system worked quite well as I never got the same robin twice because they were quite content to stay put in the cage once fed. When in the box I got confused as to which fledgling had been fed and which hadn't. They were identical.

They soon learned to fly and occasionally I propped open the door of the cage and allowed all five robins out into the room together. The cage was on Eric's bed during the day, against the wall, and they shot out into the room in different directions like an explosion of popcorn, fluttering and hopping about like five animated little speckled balls.

Of course Eric had to appear one day just as this had happened.

'What's going on?' he wanted to know. 'The room seems to be full of birds? Get off!' – one cheeky robin landed on his head, 'I'm in a hurry.'

I knew what he meant. One got the impression there were about twenty robins in the room, but I think Eric agreed that they were really very sweet and so tame and friendly.

Two days later I was in slight trouble.

'Darling, have you seen my green socks?' he called from the bedroom.

'Socks? Er, which ones do you mean?'

'The dark green ones . . . you know, the woolly ones I like. They were in the drawer here.'

I went into his room and looked in the drawer. 'Do you mean these?' I asked, fishing a pair out from the back.

'No, not those new ones . . . the old ones that . . . oh, here's one of them. But where's the other.' He held up a limp green sock, hunting for its mate.

I gulped. 'I've, er, borrowed it.'

'*Borrowed* it? What d'you mean?'

'Well, I thought you didn't wear those any more,' I said weakly but honestly. 'And I wanted a second woolly sock to put on the Tin Lizzie hot-water bottle. To keep it warm and cosy.'

'Oh, no. You knew those were my favourite socks.' He snatched another pair out of the drawer muttering 'bloody birds' as he sat grumpily on the edge of the bed tugging them on.

Over the years quite a few more woolly socks were to disappear . . .

After ten days I moved the family into Clara's old cage, a vacancy having occurred. They had much more room in there, of course. They were precocious youngsters, already showing signs of the characteristic cockiness of their species. One took to flying high up on to the central heating pipes near my ceiling and each time I got it down it flew straight back up there again, stubbornly declining my invitation to come down and get in the cage with the others – or else!

In order to get to know the little birds as individuals I put coloured PVC rings on their legs; a different colour for each bird. Then I gave them names. There was Bluebell (blue); Buttercup (yellow); Daisy (white); Marigold (orange); and Leaf (green). This also made life much easier when it came to feeding the growing youngsters – now they were flying all over the place, shooting out whenever I opened the door; as often as not, I wasn't sure which I'd fed and which I hadn't again.

I began to learn things about them. For instance, I learned that the robin that would fly up on to the pipes was Daisy, and the one that disliked meat was Buttercup, who was also the quiet one – she often stayed in the cage while the others flew around. If a second robin joined Daisy on the pipes it was always Marigold.

Bluebell and Marigold would now accept small worms but the other three still disliked them. They all loved Felix rabbit-flavoured dry cat food soaked in water until soft, too, and Daisy had gone mad on bread-and-milk.

So instead of just a family of young robins they had become individuals, each little bird different.

After I'd had them three weeks they at last began feeding themselves from the small dishes I'd been hopefully leaving in the cage for some time. Oh, happy day!

Everyone who came loved my young robins. 'Aaa . . . aren't they sweet! Just look at them!' My friends and people bringing other birds all cooed – just as they had done over baby Wol.

Wol and Stikki thought the young robins would be sweet, too . . . in their food bowl! They used to watch the antics of the little birds round the room and I'm sure I saw Wol smacking what passed as lips on more than one occasion.

As they grew older the robins started squabbling amongst themselves in the cage. They also developed the natural curiosity of their species. If I had a cardboard-box with some bird inside on the floor or on a chair it wasn't long before a robin would come and perch on the edge, head on one side, peering down into the box to see what was in there. I remember one such box contained two young blackbirds who promptly reached upwards, gaping, and squeaked loudly for food on seeing the young nosey-parker robin; the latter seemed to find this even more intriguing, gazing down at them for several minutes.

One month after they were brought to me the five little robins, all fine and healthy, flew from my window. They went in dribs and drabs during the morning and afternoon, Leaf remaining until the following morning. I saw them later in the garden, flitting about in the lilac bushes and fruit trees, some of them clicking away as robins do. They seemed fine, and I was satisfied that by then they were well able to fend for themselves.

I was pleased I'd been able to rear all five successfully.

One cold day the following winter I saw Marigold on my windowsill outside, resplendent with a red breast, now, of course. But it turned out that 'she' was a male. When spring came he brought a mate and fed her tit-bits on the sill. I saw them both frequently after this, until early summer that year, when the pair disappeared, presumably to raise a family.

=17=

WOOLLY BABIES WITH BIG FEET

LIVING near the River Thames and several lakes and water-filled quarries I naturally got a fair number of water-birds brought me – or those associated with water.

One day Eric came back from the garage holding a little kingfisher. The bird was dead, having flown straight at one of the large plate-glass windows in the garage and been killed instantly.

'I thought you'd like to see it,' he said. 'Beautiful little bird, isn't it?'

I had never seen a kingfisher close to before and I stared at it for several minutes, marvelling at its beauty as well as its practical design for fish-catching; the dazzling colours and iridescence of the feathers, the compact body, tiny feet and stubby tail and the dagger-like beak, thinner than I'd realized. Burying it, I felt infinitely sad that such a beautiful little bird should have died in such a way. Unfortunately birds of all kinds fly into plate-glass windows quite often, seeing their own reflections, often with fatal results.

The fiercest bird I ever had was a great crested grebe. Slightly injured, he was only with me two days, but during that short time he just about pecked my hand to bits, hurrying down the length of the longish rectangular box he was in to attack me even if I opened the flap of the box for a mere two seconds to place food or water inside. And he kept pecking, over and over again, until the hand was withdrawn. He even pecked through the thick gloves I was reduced to wearing, and I was really glad to be able to release him safely on the river one morning. He rushed on to the water and sailed straight up the very centre of the river as fast as he could paddle, as if defying any motor-launch or boat to hit him. Back home it took quite some time for my poor sore hands to heal. He was *not* one of my favourite patients.

My bell rang one afternoon and hurrying to the front door I found a young couple on the doorstep. Each held a small black woolly ball: moorhen chicks.

'We found them drowning in the river,' the girl with wet hair and tight blue jeans said.

'*Drowning?*' I queried in some surprise.

'Yes,' the young fellow with her insisted. 'That's right. They were caught in a swift current and were being swept away up the river.'

'They kept going right under – they were really struggling and drowning,' the girl added. 'But we managed to fish them out from the boat. Do you think they'll be all right?' She looked up at me anxiously, holding up a chick in cupped hands.

I said I'd do my best.

'We'll come back and see how they're getting on,' the youngsters called as they turned to go. 'Hope they'll be all right.'

So did I. Ironically, whenever anyone said they'd call back the bird usually died before they could do so. I don't know why but it always seemed to happen that way.

I examined my two new charges. They were each about the size of a small hen's egg, inky-black, woolly, and egg-shaped with bright-yellow pointed little beaks with scarlet tips, short black legs and enormous feet, their long, thin double-jointed toes reminding me of shiny sticks of liquorice. They were both soaking wet and cold and the head of one chick was lolling ominously on its scraggy little neck – it didn't look at all well.

Soon I got them fixed up in the usual warm box with hay, hot-water bottle and blue woolly hat. They snuggled up together under the hat, cosy and warm, and after a while they were dry again, the one with the wobbly head already looking better. I fed them a mixture of Farex and chick crumbs, opening their reluctant little beaks with the cocktail stick usually used for this purpose; one had to be very careful and gentle.

The two chicks called incessantly with the 'too-eee' call of young moorhens. I christened them Sambo and Topsy, continuing to feed them at intervals during the days that followed. They were comical little things and both did well, after that first day.

Right from the first the chicks showed completely different characters. Topsy was quiet, aloof and rather unco-operative while Sambo was just the opposite: boisterous, greedy and very affectionate. He apparently became devoted to me, climbing up my arm whenever I reached into their box to be cuddled or caressed and never seeming happy unless he was close to me. He would even climb my leg if I sat, legs outstretched, in an armchair and then climb from my lap up to my chest, finally coming to rest under my chin or against one ear, where he'd settle for a snooze. He had the most amusing and endearing habit of waggling his tiny bony little wings behind his back. They were very small and devoid of feathers at this stage and he'd put them backwards and up, almost behind his neck, waggling them independently whenever he saw me.

Topsy, on the other hand, would look at me rather disdainfully and either hide in the woolly hat or move away; no wing-waggling for *her*!

After a few days the moorhen chicks managed to walk without falling over their own big feet – a thing they'd apparently found difficult at first. Crouching side by side on the sock-covered Tin Lizzie hot-water bottle in their box they looked like two small black balls, their long toes sticking out beyond woolly breasts like spider's legs. I was fascinated by their royal-blue eyelids; it looked for all the world as if they'd been using blue eye-shadow.

I started letting them out into the room occasionally, or took them out into the garden. Sambo never left me for a second, constantly wanting to be picked up and wing-waggling at me like mad, but Topsy walked away, exploring, struggling to get free if picked up or held in the hand. They were both scared of water. Perhaps they hadn't forgotten the river?

Soon the chicks started picking up food, Topsy preferring raw mince now while Sambo stuck to Farex and chick crumbs. As I thought that he, too, should be eating some meat I made him a kind of pink Farex-and-mince puree, and he liked this.

The older they got the more active they became and soon the two chicks were running full tilt round the much larger box I'd now put them in. It was on top of the sparrow cage, where Buzby used to be. They used to tear around the room, too, their feet making a sort of slapping noise on the carpet as they ran, bony wings outstretched. Their legs were growing longer, out of all proportion to their rather late developing bodies which were still comparatively small.

Poor Sambo, his devotion to me and his strong desire to be close to which ever part of my anatomy was nearest proved to be his undoing. The Polythene rectangular bowl, used for the ducklings, had now been turned into a kind of indoor garden; half filled with soil it was very popular with young blackbirds and starlings, who learned to dig for small worms and other insects I brought in. Early one morning I placed the two little moorhen chicks in this container on the floor near the stack of cages while I cleaned out their box on my bed. I had my back turned but I could hear the 'too-eee' noises going on behind me; they knew the Polythene bowl and quite enjoyed pecking around.

Two minutes later, engrossed in what I was doing, I moved one foot slightly to one side . . . and felt something soft underneath. I lifted it immediately, then stared down in horror at the crushed little body of Sambo on the floor. Unknown to me he must have clambered out of the bowl and stood next to my foot – the only part of me he could reach. I bent and picked him up; he was still alive but died seconds later in my hand. I was wearing soft slippers at the time but my weight had killed him.

Naturally I was extremely upset and shed bitter tears as I buried the pathetic little black woolly body in the garden. It seemed so ironic that the affectionate chick had died so tragically while the aloof don't-touch-me one had been spared. For a minute I was guilty of the uncharitable thought: why did it have to be Sambo?

Five days later we went on holiday to Devon and Topsy came with us, together with two little sparrows, Chip and Cheeky, a song-thrush and a greenfinch. Wol and Stikki were being looked after by the RSPCA and Pam had taken Crusoe and several other birds. It was quite a business, arranging it all.

'Must we take all this lot?' demanded Eric, packing the car. 'Bloody birds are taking up all the room.'

'There's only *three* boxes – they can go on the back seat,' I said.

'Where are we going to put these then?' he asked, holding a box of picnic things, two large flasks, some boots, two rugs and about four coats. 'Can't the birds go on the floor?' He was getting annoyed and banging things around. The car, like my room, seemed to be bursting at the seams.

'No, they can't . . . it'd be too bumpy and draughty for them, poor little things,' I said indignantly. 'Besides, there's shoes and things down there.' I always took everything but the kitchen sink, my excuse being that you never knew what the weather was going to do and I liked to be prepared for all eventualities.

'Wouldn't it be nice if we could go without *any* birds,' Eric grumbled as we finally got under way.

I didn't answer. Secretly I was wishing we could take all of them. I was already worrying about whether Pam would give Crusoe his cheese at lunchtime and whether Wol and Stikki would be happy.

I'd had to leave Topsy's large box behind but Ivy solved the problem on our arrival by producing a pen designed for two gerbils she'd once had, made by her son. It was a large rectangular wire frame with a hardboard floor and when fitted out for Topsy with lots of newspaper, a hay bed, paddling bowl, etc., proved to be ideal. About three feet long, it gave the young moorhen plenty of room to run up and down; she was very active now and made full use of it.

A few days later my friend's husband, Bob, reading in the lounge underneath my bedroom put down his paper and looked up.

'What's that thumping noise upstairs?' he asked. 'Sounds like someone running up and down.'

'Oh, it's Topsy, I expect. My moorhen.'

'*Moorhen?*' he exclaimed. 'What – has it got boots on or something?'

We all laughed but Bob took a lot of convincing that it was only one small moorhen chick with big floppy feet.

The sparrows shared a box cage with the greenfinch, all three making themselves at home and twittering around quite happily, as they'd also done during the long car journey. Unlike Chirpy, these sparrows were completely unaffected by colour, so there was no problem there.

My husband, hoping I knew for a more or less bird-free holiday that year, was out of luck, as it happened, because I inadvertently got involved with two pigeons in one week. The first I came across in an alleyway in Plymouth while we were shopping there one day. I could see at a glance the bird was ill so I picked it up and carried it back to the car. Later, I met Eric in a pre-arranged place.

'I've ... er ... had to leave the car window open a little,' I announced as we walked along.

He stopped and stared at me. 'Why?'

'Well, there's a pigeon inside.'

'Oh, no!' he groaned. 'Not another bird. What's the matter with it?'

'I don't know. I think it may have eaten poison or something.'

We drove back the seventeen miles to our friend's house with the pigeon in a box, obtained from the first grocer we passed, and I did what I could for the bird – but it died in the night.

Two days later we drove the nine miles to the coast, as usual, and I left Eric sunning himself on the cliff while I went to buy something at the small seaside shop. I was just crossing the narrow lane at the bottom of the long steep hill down to the car park when I saw another pigeon. It was a racing pigeon, this time, with a metal ring and it looked exhausted. It was also in great danger of being run over as it was standing in the road. I carried it the short distance to the car, plonked it on the rear window ledge inside and gave it crumbs and water; fortunately we had picnic things in the boot. Then I went to where Eric was lying with closed eyes.

'I've . . . er . . . had to leave the car window open again,' I murmured apologetically, sitting on the grass beside him.

He rose up on one elbow. 'What . . . again? I don't believe it! Not *another* bird? What's the matter this time?'

'It's just tired . . . and hungry. It's a racing pigeon. Must be lost.'

Back at the house I settled the pigeon for the night and early next morning – after it had had a good rest and food – I released it outside where it flew on to the roof. Eric and our friends stood watching. After a few minutes we went indoors for breakfast.

'It'll stay up there a while and then circle around to get its bearings before heading for its loft,' said Ivy knowingly as she poured out the tea. She had had lost pigeons before, she explained, and this was always what happened.

I might have known it wouldn't happen this time. There are always exceptions to the rule.

After breakfast we all trooped outside to see if the bird had gone. It had. There was no sign of it anywhere. It was a perfect day, sunny with a cloudless blue sky and gentle breeze and we set off for the beach. That evening, shortly after we got back, two small boys appeared at the garden gate. One of them was holding a very wet and bedraggled pigeon; no need to ask *what* pigeon!

'Where did you find it?' I asked with sinking heart. The boys were from next door.

'It fell into our goldfish pond,' was the rather strange reply as they handed me the bird.

I wondered why a pigeon that should have been on its way home had been lingering near a small pond? Bit odd.

Ivy came out and joined us. She'd been at home all day, not being much of a one for the seaside. 'It's been hanging around all day,' she said. 'Doesn't seem to know where to go.'

I carried the pigeon inside and put it back in the box.

Four days and umpteen telephone calls later it was reunited with its owner thirty miles away in Exeter. He said it was a young bird and wasn't supposed to have been flying anywhere; it had disappeared from the loft roof with some others. He said he'd lost over twenty pigeons that day and this one came from good stock; he was glad to get it back.

As I lay in bed that night I couldn't help wondering if the other pigeons had all flown to the seaside somewhere too? If they had, I hoped I wouldn't meet up with them.

I didn't think Eric could stand many more.

=18=

TOPSY GROWS UP

BACK home after our holiday I installed Topsy in the now empty sparrow cage. Charlie had sadly died and the others either flown or been moved elsewhere, and Chip and Cheeky liked the smaller cage they'd travelled in. Wol, Stikki, Crusoe and the others were all back in their old cages; I was glad to see them again.

The young moorhen was growing fast now, with grey breast feathers and long, sturdy legs. The door of the cage was usually left open except at night and she spent a lot of time strolling round the room and occasionally climbing on to my bed or the furniture. This was made possible by an interesting discovery I had made; namely, that she never made a mess anywhere – she was 'house-trained'. Even when she was a tiny chick I noticed that whenever she was 'taken short' she rushed to the nearest dish of water and used that as a lavatory, and as she grew older she continued to act in the same way, her 'lavatory' being an old Polythene washing-up bowl of shallow water placed in a strategic position near her cage. I was delighted about this, a house-trained moorhen being something I certainly hadn't anticipated. It seemed almost too good to be true. The bowl, of course, had to be emptied frequently and she had another, just inside her cage, for paddling in and drinking. She ate a good deal of greenstuff now, lettuce, water-cress and any pond-weed I cared to fetch. This was always put in the paddling bowl.

When Topsy took a nap on my bed – she favoured the old red cushion Chirpy was so fond of – I always made sure there was a clean bowl of shallow water up there as well, and this was used, when necessary. I was most impressed with her cleanliness, I must say. So, I think, was Eric.

When she was fully fledged two weeks later I tried the moorhen on the children's paddling pool – similar to the one the eight ducklings had been on – in the garden, but she never liked this. She just floated about unenthusiastically, looking bored and unhappy and never attempting to swim or dive. She didn't seem to care for the garden at all, come to think of it.

Indoors it was a different matter. She was very active, jumping up and down on the bed and flying on to the back of a chair to perch on occasions. She was more affectionate now, too, and if I lay on my side on the bed, my head at the foot of the divan, Topsy would jump up, walk stealthily round to the back of my neck and try to squeeze under my head, her sharp little beak and cold toes pushing and wriggling until I lifted it, all this accompanied by incessant and urgent 'too-eee' noises. As soon as I raised my head she curled up and slept exactly where it had been, presumably because it had left a nice warm dent. This was fine for Topsy but it left my head with nowhere to go! She objected to being used as a pillow and didn't approve of me moving away, either. So I had to twist my head backwards, just behind her body; it was most uncomfortable.

The moorhen was a great one for warmth and comfort at this stage and another habit of hers occurred in the early morning. She would lift one outsize foot and bang the wire door of her cage when she considered it was time to get up – usually long before I did – and, reaching out of bed, I just managed to release the catch and open the door for her without getting out of bed. Then I snuggled down for another snooze. At least, that was always my intention. I would hear Topsy tearing up and down the room a few times and then, after a short pause, I'd hear her give a fluttery jump on to the foot of my bed. Another pause, then stealthy footsteps – she always walked on my bed in this strange stealthy manner – approached the pillow. So slowly and cautiously was this done it was almost as if she were trying not to wake me, I used to think. At last she reached the head of the bed and her tactics changed; a quick scramble and dive and there she was between the sheets, her icy-cold black rubbery toes nestled cosily under my chin and her sharp little claws sticking in the tender skin of my throat like eight sharp needles.

'Why do you put up with it?' exclaimed Eric when I remarked casually how cold and painful it was. 'You're mad! Throw her out!' But of course I couldn't . . . and didn't. I was very fond of her.

Topsy went through this procedure every morning for several weeks, protesting with angry cries if ever I did try to move her. 'Now come on, Topsy. I've got to get up,' I'd insist, but my funny moorhen wasn't pleased at all.

If she'd been human I'm sure she'd have pleaded, 'Just *five* more minutes?'

In the autumn she completed her first moult and developed the brilliant flame-coloured shield – the horny structure at the top of the beak. I took a photograph of this but for some unknown reason it came out disappointingly white.

Early one morning Topsy literally went berserk, flying round the room and crashing into things, crying in distress. I knew at once what it was; she'd virtually gone wild overnight and desperately wanted to go. Jumping out of bed, I dressed quickly, put the young moorhen in a box and carried her across the field to the lake. I'd vowed I'd never again put ducklings over there, but moorhens seemed safe enough. There were quite a few to be seen on the water and near one of the tiny islands, including some youngsters about her age.

Topsy jumped out of the box and swam into a dense clump of reeds in some shallow water. Moorhens usually favoured this spot and often headed for the reeds when I approached. I waited for a few minutes, watching movement in the rushes and listening to the occasional cry of a water-bird in the still morning air. There was a mist over the pony field and it was very quiet; no one was around yet.

Topsy didn't appear again so I turned for home, satisfied that she'd be all right. Of course I thought about the missing ducklings. I didn't think I'd ever again go over to the lake without pondering on the subject – there were so many memories.

Topsy's sudden wildness was really no surprise; wild birds often went like this. They could be tame, affectionate and perfectly happy and content with me one minute, then, one day, they suddenly changed completely and didn't appear to know me any more, becoming terrified at the very sight of me in the room.

'Ungrateful thing!' Eric said on more than one occasion. 'After all you've done for it – it just flies off like that!'

But I got used to it, though I must admit I felt quite upset when it first happened.

I reckoned it was a young adult's way of letting you know it was ready for its freedom.

=19=

TOM AND THE SNAILS

TOM was the song-thrush who came on holiday with us. He had been brought to me previously by an elderly couple who said they found him in the road.

'He kept trying to hop and fell over all the time, dear,' the rather timid grey-haired lady told me.

'Yes, that's right,' confirmed her husband, a tubby gentleman in a peaked yachting cap. 'Can't seem to stand up properly.'

I saw what they meant when I placed Tom on the floor. He had thin, weak little legs and when he attempted to hop forwards he tipped up on to his beak. He was only a fledgling but it was as if his legs simply couldn't support the weight of his small body.

I put the young thrush in the old budgie cage, which he grew to love – it was surprising how popular this cage was – and fed him the same crushed yeast tablets I'd given to Chirpy, hoping the Vitamin B would strengthen his legs, too. I mixed the powder in with his raw mince. After four days his legs really did seem stronger and he could stand without falling over, though he was still a little wobbly.

Tom developed normally, practised his flying across the room and a week later was perching and roosting like any other fledgling; before this he'd remained on the floor of the cage, even at night. He became very tame and used to fly over and snuggle into a cushion placed behind my pillow early mornings, sometimes snoozing under my chin or against my ear, making the familiar thrush 'tseek, tseek' noise all the time. He was a dear little bird, though not at all like Kweekie in character.

I was pleased with Tom's improvement and progress and I thought his troubles were over and that one day he'd be able to be released and able to fend for himself. But alas, almost a month to the day he came I suddenly noticed he had difficulty in perching. Examining him, I found that the hind toe of his right foot was bent forwards and was sticking up between the front toes. I didn't like the look of this at all. The other foot was still normal, however, and wonderfully adaptable as birds are, Tom soon learned to manage gripping the perch with just his one good foot. Exactly one month later the hind toe of the other foot went forward in the same way, and now poor Tom was in trouble; he found perching at all really difficult.

I adapted his cage, making him special inch-wide flat perches covered with thin foam rubber and he seemed to appreciate this innovation and managed to perch more comfortably without falling.

There was nothing wrong with the little thrush's appetite, though, but it was three months before he'd feed himself. Like Kweekie he flew to me to be fed all the time, 'tseek, tseeking' in my ear and pulling my hair impatiently. Unlike Kweekie he developed a positive passion for snails, though as with the former he never liked worms. It was interesting to compare the two birds.

Tom's appetite for snails became so insatiable that I was at a loss to know how to keep up with it. He liked most other insects too, and kept me busy searching for these in the garden. I put them in the soil-filled Polythene 'garden box' and he quickly descended on it and ate every creepy-crawly in sight, digging and poking around and bashing the snails on the flat 'anvil' stone provided.

He loved the sun and whenever I could I took the young thrush out into the garden to sunbathe or peck around on the lawn. Or put his cage in the sun in my room.

Autumn came and I hoped we wouldn't get too many early frosts; what would I do when the snails hid themselves away? So far our neglected rockery and other parts of the garden had produced plenty but I dreaded the supply running out. Tom really loved his snails and I felt so sorry about his poor feet that I did my utmost to keep my little friend happy. I had to be very careful with the snails, though. Never shall I forget that awful night when I stepped out of bed in the small hours to get a drink of water without putting on the light. Something crushed under my bare foot . . . it was a large snail. Ugh! Hastily putting on my bedside lamp I saw to my horror that there were snails everywhere: crawling on the carpet, climbing the walls, up the legs of the table and even under my bed. I had forgotten to round up Tom's left-overs! I removed all the snails I could find, peering under and around my bed with a torch; I didn't fancy any climbing into bed with me when I finally put out the light.

Next morning Eric sat down to breakfast, gripping the sides of the table to pull it closer to him. The fingers of one hand closed over something cold and hard.

'Do you mind removing *this*?' he demanded in icy tones, picking off the miscreant from where it was hiding. He held the snail out gingerly, as if expecting it to bite, a look of disgust on his face.

'Oh, sorry . . . I must have missed that one,' I apologized.

This incident taught me a lesson and from then on I kept a large jar with holes punched in the lid. Any snail that Tom hadn't eaten by bedtime was caught and placed in this jar for the night.

'What on earth are you doing?' asked Eric, frowning as he looked up and saw me crouching low over the garden box one evening muttering to myself.

'Counting. Tom's snails. Five empty shells . . . that means there's another three live ones somewhere . . . oh, there're two of them. Now where's the other . . .?' I continued mumbling to myself; this was to be a nightly ritual.

'There's one over there!' said Eric, sitting forward pointing a moment later. 'For heaven's sake . . . must we have snails all over the room?'

'It's all right, I've got them all now, see?' I held up the jar.

'Well, I hope so.'

I always put a lettuce leaf in the jar, too, for the snails to eat. Their days might be numbered but I didn't want to deprive them of their last supper. Keeping them in a jar overnight also meant my young thrush had fresh snails for breakfast, which I'm sure he appreciated.

As the evenings drew in I developed a routine, so snail-conscious did I become. About half an hour after it grew dark I went creeping out into the garden, a torch in one hand and the snail jar in the other, to search for the creatures. This was the best time to find them, especially if there had been rain. The snails, all shapes and sizes, came out foraging for food and, apart from satisfying Tom, I felt I was doing the garden a good turn; indeed, I was alarmed to find snails galore, all over the place, munching away at all my favourite plants.

When the weather grew colder, however, they became harder to find. Tom expected at least ten small snails for supper, or four or five large ones, and he definitely looked very disgruntled if presented with only one or two miserable specimens. However, just when things were beginning to get desperate and I could hardly look him in the eye I had a stroke of luck; I found a cache of large, dormant snails packed tightly together and wedged between an old stone sink and a low brick wall. I had to kneel on the gravel path and reach into a narrow gap, picking off as many snails as I needed but so many were there that, with rationing, this hiding place provided snails for almost the entire winter.

Tom was delighted and so was I; the snails were probably less pleased. Many a winter's night I sat back watching television with vigorous snail-hammering as the background music – my own private Anvil Chorus!

In the spring that followed poor Tom developed arthritis in his legs and his toes were all screwed up like small, clenched fists. He could hardly perch at all now. I put a piece of foam-backed carpet in his cage changing and washing it daily, and also made him a special soft foam cushion to rest on and eventually he got used to this further disability. He never lost his tremendous appetite nor his zest for living, remaining alert, bright-eyed and interested in everything that went on in the room. I was assured by the vet that bird's legs being very different from ours and with fewer nerve endings the little thrush was not in pain as we know it; I believe he suffered mostly from discomfort and annoyance. I wrote to a great bird-lover with a lifetime of experience in dealing with injured birds explaining in detail all about Tom and asking if she thought it would be kinder to have him put to sleep. She wrote back saying she thought my little thrush would let me know when life held no more for him, and that until then I was doing the right thing in caring for him so well. I felt reassured.

The deterioration of his legs continued and soon Tom had to be propped in an upright position or he fell over. No longer could he fly; there was nothing wrong with his wings but he had no 'under-carriage' to land on. I even had to smash his snails for him now – *not* my favourite job – as he invariably fell over if he tried. I made him a kind of nest in an old baking-tin and Tom spent most of the day in this, watching everything. I could place him in the sun, or near the fire if it was chilly, and he seemed perfectly content, calling for food when hungry like a baby bird again. On warm days I took him into the garden.

One evening when he was about fifteen months old Tom had a series of violent convulsions and died. He had been demanding and eating food only a few minutes before they started and it was a great shock, the suddenness of the attack. I had no warning that it was about to happen. I was terribly upset. I am certain though that in spite of increasing disabilities my charming song-thrush enjoyed his short life with me. I buried him beside little Chirpy under the fallen tree and made the front of Eric's jersey soggy with my tears.

Bing Crosby died the same day, the news of his death coming over the radio as I helplessly watched Tom's convulsions. It was a sad day.

=20=

EGBERT
THE ECCENTRIC DRAKE

HE was the smallest mallard duckling I'd ever seen, about half the size of a normal, newly hatched one. Spiky and bedraggled, he was too weak even to stand and frankly I didn't give much for his chance of survival. The man who brought me the duckling explained. Apparently there was a mallard's nest at the bottom of his garden, near the river. The mother duck, having successfully hatched thirteen eggs, had apparently decided enough was enough and had set off down the river with her new brood leaving the fourteenth egg unhatched in the deserted nest. That evening the man was strolling round his garden when he spotted the last little duckling struggling from its egg. Hoping to save its life, the rest of the mallard family having long since disappeared from sight, he brought it to me.

Egbert, as I called him, was the thirteenth duckling I'd been brought in three years: *not* a good start in life for him. But that tiny weak duckling was to turn into one of the largest, plumpest mallard drakes imaginable and turned out to be the greatest and most eccentric character of them all.

But to go back to that June evening.

I put the tiny duckling in a box with the old Tin Lizzie and covered him with the soft blue woolly many-times-washed hat.

'We don't want any more ducklings,' said Eric firmly, frowning at him. 'He may be very sweet and all that but . . .'

'Well, we've *got* him,' I interrupted him in mid-grumble. 'I couldn't refuse to take the poor little thing, now could I?'

'Hmmmph,' snorted Eric, turning away.

'Besides, he may not live anyway. He's very small and weak.'

I sighed. Eric was always we-don't-want-any-more-ing. I was used to it, but I still found it slightly irritating.

Little Egbert had to be coaxed to eat anything at all, so weak and miserable was he, but I managed to open his beak and feed him soggy chick crumbs at intervals. Mallard ducklings are tough little things – they have to be, to survive in the wild – and I hoped for the best, watching over him like an anxious hen those first few days and making sure he was always warm and comfortable. After two days he stood for the first time on his wobbly little webbed feet and seemed slightly stronger, but it was two weeks before he really seemed to grow at all.

After that time, however, Egbert decided to grow and he certainly made up for lost time. He was running about in a large cardboard-box pen, now, and behaving more like a normal duckling. I was delighted with his progress and the fact that he was still very much alive; it had been touch and go.

As the weeks went by Egbert spent more and more time with me in the garden. He followed me everywhere, running full tilt after me across the lawn and sleeping close to my face if I lay on a rug in the sun as I did for a while most sunny afternoons. I always preferred lying on the grass to sitting in a deck-chair.

I had three other mallard ducklings I was rearing that year; Egbert, however, was nearly a month younger than any of them and, being small for his age, got bullied and pecked even by the youngest duckling if ever I tried them all together. So he became 'mother's boy', leaving the others swimming in the plastic pool or running round the wire enclosure while he kept close to my side on the lawn, like a tiny shadow.

He was different from the others in other ways, too. For instance, he wasn't particularly interested in water and never really liked the pool, as all the other ducklings I'd ever had had done. He preferred human company, becoming very friendly with anyone in the garden and running over to see them, as he got older.

'Hello, Egbert,' the other tenants would call as he waddled to greet them. 'How are you today?'

He was very inquisitive and liked to see what people were doing. During the summer quite a few people came outside to sit in deck-chairs or lie on the lawn, and once when I heard a little scream from behind a bush I found my precocious duckling fiddling with his beak at the bottom half of a girl's bikini.

'I was lying there with my eyes closed,' laughed a surprised Lynda. 'He woke me up! Honestly, Egbert – you are awful!'

When he was about six weeks old and almost adult Egbert showed

just how different he was from your run-of-the-mill young mallard, for
he developed a passion for wet washing. He liked to nibble it. One side
of the garden there were five clothes lines in a square with a diagonal
and this became his favourite place. He became a fanatical wet-
washing nibbler. The second one of the tenants in the house came
across the garden with a bowl of newly washed laundry Egbert waddled
full tilt after them to the clothes lines. If he could, he nibbled the
washing in the bowl on the ground before it was even hung up and
once after a loud 'Hey!' I turned and saw him hurrying away with
someone's wet bra gripped firmly in his beak, the owner giving chase.

But what he really liked best of all was the washing dripping on him
after it had been pegged to the line. He would stand happily
underneath the lines all day. He preferred nice flapping wet sheets and
the dangling sleeves of shirts and jumpers, given the choice, making
the edges muddy with his beak, as often as not, because when he
wasn't nibbling washing Egbert was usually prodding around the grass
and borders for worms and other delicacies and his beak got very
muddy.

The young drake lived in the garden now, sleeping in the big hutch
in the shed at night. He became a bit of a menace over the washing and
I tried hard to discourage him, but it was no use.

'He'll get us into trouble,' warned Eric, waggling a finger at me one
day. 'You mark my words.'

For once I was inclined to agree. Sometimes I had to creep out into
the garden with a bowl of detergent and a small scrubbing brush and
hastily scrub the bottom of some article that Egbert had seen fit to
decorate with a muddy, scalloped border. Then I rinsed it, hoping and
praying it would dry again before the owner came out. I remember he
was obsessed with a girl's check cotton dress; wet and flapping in the
breeze, it seemed to attract him like a magnet. It was only much later I
learned that she sometimes had to wash it twice in one day.

The saddest sight I ever saw at that time was Egbert standing under
the clothes line on a wet day. Alone and desolate, he'd stand there
nearly all day, waiting in vain. One day I hit on an idea; as one
sometimes does, I wondered why I hadn't thought of it before. Cutting
an old sheet into strips I pegged one of them, to the line for my awful
young drake to nibble. Egbert was delighted, especially when autumn
came and fewer people hung out washing. He stood there contentedly
nibbling away for hours on end, the strip of sheet getting muddier and
muddier and I hoped I'd at last solved the problem.

Egbert had a friend called Winnie. She was a young pigeon we'd found while out shopping one Saturday afternoon where she was making an abortive attempt to fly over or on to a too-high wall, banging her poor head repeatedly against the bricks and falling to the ground. Over and over again she did this, becoming so dazed that I picked her up before she did some permanent brain damage; pigeons are not the brightest of birds. I brought her home.

She was a pretty bird, pinky-beige in colour, and I kept her two weeks in the large cardboard top cage before releasing her in the garden. But, as with all pigeons, Winnie hung around, roosting close to my window at night. And one day she met Egbert. I hadn't realized their friendship until one day when I happened to glance out of my window and saw the two birds strolling side by side across the lawn. After that I saw them together often and they seemed to be great friends; if not actually with Egbert on the ground, Winnie was never far away, perched in a tree or on the fence.

When the weather grew colder Winnie came back indoors again to sleep, spending part of each day in her old cage and part of it in the garden. If Egbert was different from other mallards then Winnie was different, too, from other pigeons, for she loved dancing round the room with me and took a particular liking to a certain tune. While doing the chores I sometimes danced around to some old dance band records, not being a pop fan, to cheer myself up. The first time I did this when Winnie was in the room I noticed she had become very agitated in her cage, pacing up and down like a caged lion and obviously wanting to get out. Opening the cage door she flew straight to my shoulder and crouched there while I continued dancing. As she found it difficult to balance as I waltzed merrily around with the duster I took her in my cupped hands, holding her close . . . and discovered she loved it! From then on Winnie's daily dances became a regular thing. She seemed to take a great liking to an old tune by the late Noel Coward called 'A Room with A View' and whenever I played, hummed, whistled or sang this tune Winnie became very excited. It got so that I only had to sing a few bars of this loudly out of the window to have her fly back in from wherever she was, if she was outside. She never reacted in this way to any other tune. On several occasions when I couldn't find her and got rather anxious because of the cats, I went into the field and sang her favourite tune at the top of my voice. It worked like magic, Winnie flying to me within seconds even when she'd obviously been some way away.

Meanwhile, Egbert had taken up jogging. He looked fat and very handsome now, with most of his bottle-green head and neck feathers and drake's colouring, including the tightly curled central tail feathers. He wouldn't complete all his green head feathers until the spring.

Every day now he followed me across the garden and under the barbed-wire fence into the field, quacking away excitedly all the while as he always did in my company. Then we went for a short jog diagonally across the big field towards the centre and back, Egbert keeping pace beside me with his large, compact body rocking like a boat as he hurried along, quacking incessantly. It was his idea that we went diagonally; if I attempted to go round the edge he stopped dead and refused to come. Sometimes he decided on a more leisurely walk across the field, refusing to hurry. He had a mind of his own, did Egbert, and always knew exactly what he wanted to do and what he didn't.

After a few weeks of this exercise – I must have lost pounds in weight – Egbert decided to change the routine. He'd accompany me as usual towards the middle of the field but instead of turning and waddling back to the garden he now went for a fly round each day. He stopped dead, facing towards the woods, then turned his head this way and that, neck stretched forward parallel to the ground. This was always his prelude to flying. He ignored me completely, taking no notice of whether I'd started back to the garden or not, then suddenly he'd take off.

Egbert's flying was somewhat haphazard; sometimes I wondered whether there was something wrong with his eyesight but I came to the conclusion he just liked to live dangerously. He seemed to delight in flying very fast straight at some thicket or clump of trees, swerving and gaining height in the last possible minute to avoid them. Sometimes he flew high directly over me as I stood in the field watching, apparently heading straight for some tall buildings and disaster. 'Egbert!' I'd yell, waving my arms. 'This way!' but he'd peel off in true Battle of Britain fashion in the last second and land calmly and safely by the clothes line in the garden.

Usually Egbert flew in a wide arc heading towards the woods and lake and then turning abruptly and flying round and over the ditch and thicket dividing the large and small fields and then another tight turn and up through a narrow gap in the tall elms bordering our garden to land with a plop on the lawn. By the time I got back, puffing and blowing, he was nonchalantly drinking water or preening his feathers just as if he'd never been anywhere; usually he waddled over to meet me, quacking, as much as to say, 'What kept you?'

As the weeks went by Egbert grew even more daring, flying

sometimes in a figure of eight round the field and surrounding countryside. Occasionally he approached the garden too fast and had to jam on his brakes suddenly to land almost vertically, like a helicopter. On several occasions he overshot and landed in the next-door garden. Once I heard a splintering of twigs as if he'd misjudged his distance and crashed through a hedge or trees. Hurrying back to the field I had my heart in my mouth, wondering if he'd broken his wing or something. But my amusing drake was standing quietly on the lawn completely unruffled.

Egbert simply hated frost and snow. The first time he saw the former covering the lawn he waddled back into the shed again and refused to come out until coaxed. He obviously didn't consider grass covered with white frost fit to walk on, and he took a very poor view indeed of the plastic paddling pool being frozen, having now got quite fond of it and accustomed to taking a daily dip each morning.

Snow, Egbert decided, was far worse; he flatly refused to tread on it at all, standing miserably in the shed until I lifted him out and set him down gently on the lawn, speaking to him soothingly. He tried walking a few steps then but collapsed in a heap, shaking all over like a jelly. 'Now, come along, Egbert – try again,' I coaxed, but no amount of persuasion would make him move another inch and I had to carry him back into the shed and produce a cosy box of hay for him to sit in. Another snowy day – we had a lot of snow that winter – Egbert actually took off from the shed and flew quacking all round the garden presumably looking for some snow-free grass to land on. He was forced to land in fairly deep snow in the end, only to pitch forward so that his head and neck momentarily disappeared from view. He was *not* amused.

One of the funniest sights I'd seen for a long time was that of my large, fat mallard drake perched on the highest point of the roof of this very tall house. Taking pity on him one cold, snowy day in January I'd had him indoors for an hour or two. Egbert didn't really care for it indoors now and soon got fidgety, so when I saw that the snow had melted on the gravel path outside my window I picked him up and popped him through thinking he'd flutter the few feet to the ground. But to my amazement he flew upwards and back over the roof, quickly disappearing from sight. I ran outside and there he was on the roof near some chimney-pots, facing down the garden and quacking, neck outstretched.

'Egbert!' I cried. 'Come on down at once, you idiot.'

He declined. He looked so funny up there that I went indoors to fetch my camera. When I came out again, Egbert had vanished.

I spent the next half hour frantically searching everywhere round the garden, fields and surrounds of the house, thinking he'd flown somewhere and got himself lost. Every now and then I peered up at the roof top from all angles, but I couldn't see him anywhere. In despair I turned dejectedly back towards the house.

Eric was standing near the front door. 'Aren't you coming to have lunch?' he asked, as if nothing was the matter.

'No,' I almost sobbed. 'I can't . . . not until I've found Egbert.'

'He's in the garden, on the lawn,' my husband said over his shoulder as he went back indoors.

Later I realized what must have happened. Egbert must have been on the flat roof bordering the glass domed roof over the centre of the house – this was invisible from the ground. He must have moved from the apex of the sloping tiled part of the roof down to this hidden part while I was indoors!

As well as a wet-washing nibbler, the young drake was also a compulsive toe nibbler, always strangely attracted to shoes and feet. As a small duckling he'd loved lying on my shoes or slippers indoors, and as he grew larger he used to drape himself over them, even preferring to lie on my kicked-off shoes in the garden rather than lying on the rug or grass. People hanging out washing made good toe-nibbling subjects, their hands being too occupied to push him away, especially if they were wearing open-toed shoes or sandals. It was no good pushing him away with your foot because Egbert only took this as an invitation to play.

Sometimes if there weren't many people around in the garden Egbert became bored and flew over the fence into the garden next door. One of his friends over there was a large chocolate-coloured dog, and another was a black cat. I was frightened they might attack him but he seemed to get on very well with both of them, even wandering into the dog's kennel on one occasion when its owner was out. And I actually saw him strolling down the garden path with the cat.

There were two gardeners next door, too, and Egbert used to hang around waiting for any worms they might dig up. And of course there was the clothes line, propped too high for him to reach the washing, thank goodness. I think they sent their sheets to the laundry.

On one occasion when I couldn't see my mischievous drake anywhere the lady next door informed me that she thought he was in their kitchen.

'I think he goes in there to listen to the radio,' she added, seriously.

With Egbert anything was possible . . .

He put the half-wild cats firmly in their place, too. Unafraid of them, he had been known to tweak their tails and even peck them on the nose if they came too close. They treated him with great respect. On occasions he even sampled their dinner, the cats standing back in awe until he chose to move away.

Friendly with everyone, Egbert especially liked children. He enjoyed a good game and being chased round the garden. He remained affectionate towards me even when fully adult, making a great fuss of me when I opened the hutch door in the morning, quacking loudly and nibbling my hands and arms. He used to court me, too, when in a gay mood; his tail would jerk forwards to meet his backward jerked head, then he'd run forwards with head and neck parallel to the ground.

During the winter I'd had to move Egbert's sleeping quarters, the big hutch, down to the bottom of the garden, as the shed was required for other things. This was a blow; the hutch wasn't waterproof and it hadn't even a covered sloping roof like a proper rabbit-hutch. I was worried about foxes, too; close to the fields, he'd be very vulnerable down there.

I would miss the shed in other ways, too. I stored my bale of hay – used in cages and boxes – in there, as well as my garden tools and many other things. Wherever could I put the hay?

First of all, though, I had to do something about the hutch. I bought a large roll of Twilweld, and one Sunday Eric helped me heave the very heavy hutch out of the shed and on to the lawn. Then we completely covered the entire thing with the wire – every inch of it – and had double Twilweld on the door. With a hammer each and a box of staples we were hammering away all afternoon. It took us hours, but in the end I was satisfied that the hutch was now well and truly fox-proof; no fox was going to eat my Egbert in the night!

The next thing to do was to make it waterproof.

'What does it matter if the rain gets in?' said Eric. 'He's a duck, isn't he? Ducks are supposed to like the rain!'

We encased the hutch in black Polythene, wrapping it up like a huge parcel. Then we heaved it up on to the wooden base – rather like a topless table – and positioned it in a corner of the garden, hidden from the house and road by a dense, bushy hedge. A sheet of tarpaulin covered the roof, held in place by bricks, and the job was done.

That night Egbert slept in there for the first time. As I turned the key in the strong padlock I felt I had done all I could and he seemed quite happy with the new arrangement.

The bale of hay was transferred to various sacks, brought indoors and squeezed into any available space. Some had to go on top of Eric's wardrobe. The rooms seemed to be full of hay, now – as well as birds! I really missed that shed.

Spring again, and the usual influx of baby birds and fledglings kept me very busy indoors. But I always kept an eye on Egbert through the window and spent at least part of each afternoon with him in the garden. He was always torn between lying with me or under the clothes lines, usually waddling backwards and forwards between the two places.

One Sunday I went down the garden early morning as usual to let him out; I remember the dew was heavy on the lawn still and my shoes got wet; it looked like being another lovely day as the sun rose across the fields to the east of me. As I approached the hutch I saw that the waterproof cover thrown over the front at night was lying on the grass; must have slipped off in the night, I thought, or perhaps the wind had got up. I walked up to the hutch and then stopped a few feet away, staring in horror. Stunned. The door had been wrenched open, the wood splintered, and my dear Egbert was gone: vandals!

I stared, barely taking it in. The padlock was still locked and clung to the metal hoop still, and on the ground lay a garden fork that had obviously been used as a lever. Normally I would have put it back in the shed, after use, but the previous day I'd been using it and left it sticking in the ground near the hutch. There was no sign of Egbert anywhere. I searched around but I knew instinctively I'd never see him again; they'd taken him. Later I noticed that there were scarcely any droppings in the hutch and his supper hadn't been eaten, so someone must have broken into the hutch shortly after I'd put him to bed the night before.

In a daze I walked back to the house. The police came and inspected the damage. Then they left, saying they'd let me know if they found the person or persons responsible. They said they thought that Egbert would almost certainly have been killed . . . and probably eaten.

The rest of the day was like a nightmare; so were the days and weeks that followed. I was heartbroken. In his prime and almost a year old, my beautiful drake had been stolen. He was such a happy fellow and so enjoyed life; it seemed too cruel. The local paper did a piece about it and I offered £50 reward for his safe return, also placing notices about this in local shop windows. But nothing happened. I never saw him again, nor heard anything at all.

People were very kind and friends did their best to console me, but I felt nothing but anger towards whoever had taken him and remorse that he had gone. It was especially hard never knowing exactly what had happened or whether he was really dead or perhaps captive somewhere. No one in the house had heard a thing, nor had the neighbours. Someone must have approached from the fields, it was thought; it was easy enough to get through the thin privet hedge which had many gaps.

Poor Egbert. I tried to find comfort in the fact that though he'd had a short life it had certainly been a gay one.

Winnie, the pigeon, seemed very lost without Egbert. She started accompanying me down the garden to the incinerator to burn the rubbish every day, as Egbert had done, perching in a nearby tree. She also came into the field with me, sometimes, and flew round in wide circles overhead as I walked, alighting on some tree branch for a rest now and again. A more conventional flyer than Egbert and not as spectacular as Jacko, she never went far but swooped and dived, flying very swiftly and treating me to quite an interesting aerial display nevertheless. Sometimes she came back indoors with me, but on other occasions she remained in the field or garden until later.

One afternoon in early June Winnie went missing. It was the hour she usually came indoors for her siesta and I was worried. I called around outside, but she didn't come, so I came and had another look indoors; no Winnie. I leaned out of the window and sang 'A Room with A View' very loudly, but there was still no sign of her. I knew then that something was wrong.

Standing outside Eric's window where I'd last seen her several hours earlier one of the wild cats hanging around gave me a clue. It was sitting near some thick shrubbery, tail neatly curled round its legs, licking its lips.

I found all that was left of poor Winnie under one of the bushes when I parted the undergrowth – a pathetic cluster of pinky-beige feathers.

It was just six weeks after Egbert was taken.

=21=

SCRAMBLED EGG
WITH EVERYTHING

THERE was never time to sit around moping in the spring and summer; there were too many mouths to feed and too many injuries to tend to. Birds were coming in daily.

One was a swift that had been found in someone's garden.

'It was on the lawn,' the lady with a little girl said as she handed me the bird in an empty tissue box. 'Our cat picked it up but I don't think it's hurt . . . we managed to get it off him straight away.'

I held the little swift in my hand and gently examined him. I was always very interested in these birds, they were so different from the usual garden birds. I always marvelled at the velvety softness of the chocolate-brown feathers, the long, beautifully tapered scimitar wings crossed over the back, the tiny, fragile beak and comparatively huge mouth and the short little feathered legs with tiny toes and needle-like claws. One reads descriptions of birds in books and sees them on television, but to actually hold the living bird in your hand makes you realize how beautifully designed they are for the life they lead.

Swifts presented certain problems as patients, though. Spending almost their entire life on the wing, they needed something to cling to in a cage, not a perch, and like all insectivorous birds they were difficult to feed. They had to be released from somewhere high up, too, as they were unable to take off from the ground because of their short legs and long tapered wings; they needed space to swoop in an arc before gaining height to circle round.

I'd made a special box which I used for swifts, house-martins and swallows, with pockets in each back corner. These consisted of strips of cardboard across the corners draped with two more soft woolly hats. My new patient rested comfortably in one of these, his tiny claws gripping the rim as he peeped out, clinging inside the pocket in a vertical position. Fortunately he seemed to be unhurt; after a day's rest I should be able to release him.

After various experiments I hit upon some food which seemed to suit these little birds. It was a kind of puree I made from Farex, pulped apple, soaked Go Cat and two drops of Abidex. I fed him this every few hours.

Next morning, sure enough, the swift was ready to go. Holding him in my hand I felt the throbbing like a small built-in dynamo that usually signifies a swift is feeling all right and will be safe to release. I'd learned that if one didn't feel this something was wrong and it was unwise to let it go, no matter how 'all right' it might look.

Climbing the two flights of stairs to the top floor bathroom, I opened the window. Facing west and high up, it was ideal for releasing these birds; there was a wide expanse of sky and few trees or buildings in the way.

I held the swift in my cupped hands, reaching through the window. Slowly I opened my fingers. 'Off you go, then. Look after yourself.' He hesitated for a few moments, large dark eyes blinking in the sudden bright sunlight, then he spread his wings and flew in a wide sweep, soon becoming just a dark speck high in the sky.

I descended the stairs, sighing with relief. If I'd been wrong about the little swift's fitness the bird would have crashed to the ground somewhere out of sight, probably, and would have died if not found. It was always a risk. But this one was fine.

Outside in the garden I looked up at the sky. There were other swifts up there, screaming and circling around; I expected my fellow had joined them.

Freddie was a blackbird but as sometimes happens he was a character – different from the other youngsters I had that year. He was the only survivor of a nest in the laurel hedge which had been attacked by a cat. He developed in the normal manner, eating raw mince and practising his flying round the room, and became very tame and friendly, as they usually did.

But one day I ran out of raw mince and it was the afternoon of early closing day.

'It's all right,' I said to Eric who had offered to try and find a butcher's shop open somewhere. 'Don't bother – I'll give him scrambled egg.'

Little did I know just what I was letting myself in for.

Freddie became a scrambled egg addict. From that day on he insisted on it for every meal, flatly refusing any other food. Morning, noon and night I was scrambling egg, his appetite being quite insatiable. My other fledglings accepted a little of the egg but still preferred mince and bread-and-milk; not Freddie! And although quite big enough and well able to feed himself, he expected me to feed him still.

When I went out I always left him a dish of scrambled egg on the table as for some unknown reason Freddie disliked eating in his cage. Returning, I usually found he'd thrown the egg all over the place, annoyed because I hadn't been around to feed him. There would be bits everywhere; on the table, floor and even on the window sill. Like Kweekie and the wayward Edna, he also played with things in the room and I'd find pencils and ornaments all over the place, often with bits of scrambled egg sticking to them. Unlike other youngsters, Freddie objected to being shut in a cage at all during the day. He was different, all right. On my return from shopping he flew straight at me, 'chook-chooking' in a most scolding manner for having left him. It was obvious he felt neglected – how about *more* scrambled egg and a little service, this time?

When he was old enough I released the young blackbird from my window. He flew straight into the trees without hesitation and I thought that was the last I'd seen of him. I put the non-stick scrambled egg saucepan away.

'I must say,' I remarked to Eric that evening, 'it's a great relief not having to make scrambled egg all day long. I was very fond of Freddie, but . . .'

'Your fault for spoiling him,' was the stern reply. 'You make a rod for your own back.'

Next morning I was awakened by urgent knocking on the door. It was the housekeeper.

'There's a bird trying to get into the front hall,' she said. 'It's banging itself against the window. Do you think it's one of yours?'

'I'll come and see.'

Putting on my dressing-gown, I hurried down the passage and across the large hall to the other side of the house, near the front door.

'There!' she cried, pointing to one of the tall windows facing west.

A blackbird was virtually flinging itself over and over again at the window, obviously trying to get in. I saw at a glance that it was Freddie.

I went outside and he allowed himself to be picked up and carried back to my room. He was very ruffled and upset, I could see, but he recovered miraculously on receipt of a good dollop of freshly scrambled eggs which he ate greedily. He seemed very tired, retiring to his cage afterwards for a long rest.

Four days later Freddie flew from my window again, after becoming very restless indoors and wanting to go. This really was the last time I'd see him, I thought. Wrong again.

Next morning there was another knock on my door.

'Sorry, but could you come again? That blackbird's in the hall now.'

Freddie had found his way through the front door and was now panicking and fluttering wildly round the hall. At least, he *had* been. By the time I came on the scene he'd flown out of the door again – the hall windows didn't open – and finally located him on the gravel path outside our rooms, standing near a bush and looking very disconsolate. I picked him up.

Eric, shaving in his room, was surprised to see my face at the window and stopped, razor in mid-air.

'What *are* you doing outside in your dressing-gown?' he asked. 'I thought you were still in bed.' He hadn't heard the carry-on in the hall, apparently.

I held up Freddie.

'Oh no, not him again!' Eric turned his eyes to the ceiling and then moved away to the wash-basin.

I popped the blackbird through my window and walked round to the front door. It was obvious what was happening. On both occasions he had been trying to get back to my room but had become confused with so many large windows facing all directions. I had a sneaking idea that his main object in returning had been to partake of his favourite food, scrambled egg. Nobody had told him it didn't grow on trees.

Freddie stayed with me another week this time and then he flew away again. Now what, I wondered? No knock on my door next morning so I slid out of bed and drew back the curtains . . . and there was Freddie on the window sill outside – ready, willing and impatient for his early morning scrambled egg. He'd found the right window at last!

Sighing deeply, I reached for the saucepan. It's a wonder it hadn't worn out. Freddie had flown in and was now 'chook-chooking' at me from the table, feet apart, head feathers erect, facing the cooker. He was hungry; would I hurry up, please?

For the next five and a half unbelievable weeks my strange young blackbird came backwards and forwards through the window for scrambled egg every day. When other birds were out in the room I kept a net curtain pinned across, but he flew in and out at other times every half hour or so, to start with, but gradually – over the weeks – less frequently. It was a question of 'chook-chook' on the sill, a short flight to the table, some quick gulps of scrambled egg, another 'chook-chook' and out and away again – the same routine each time.

As time went by I saw less and less of Freddie and as he grew older he became, inevitably, less friendly. I saw him for the last time one warm, sunny morning in June when he suddenly appeared in the open window. He saw me and stopped, hesitating and reluctant to enter the room.

'Come on then, Freddie,' I said, but he seemed to stare at me as if I were a complete, rather frightening, stranger. Then he turned and with a startled cry flew away.

I put away the non-stick saucepan. Eric didn't like scrambled-egg and I hoped it would be a long time before I got it out again. I'd been scrambling eggs for Freddie for exactly eight weeks.

=22=

STANLEY
THE PEST-CONTROLLER

'BLOODY hell!'

The cry from the next room nearly made me drop the kettle I'd been filling.

'Joan!'

What could have happened? I hurried into Eric's room, trying in that split second to remember which birds I'd got in there and visualize what awful things they might be doing.

'What's wro . . . Oh.'

Eric was standing by the wardrobe with little pieces of hay sticking to him. Hay was scattered round his feet, a few wisps even making it to the bed. The sack had fallen off the wardrobe.

'How did it happen?' I asked, bending down and clearing up what I could. 'It's never fallen down before.'

'Well it's bloody well fallen down now!' he roared, picking bits of hay out of his hair. 'The wardrobe door sticks sometimes and when I pulled at it this lot descended.' He was very annoyed. 'You'll have to put the sack somewhere else. It's ridiculous having hay up there. And what's *that* doing down there?' He nudged a small sickle sticking out from underneath his bed with his foot. 'Bloody dangerous! Nearly cut my toe off last night!'

Oh dear. When he was in this mood everything was wrong.

'I'll take the hay and sickle away . . . and bring you another cup of tea,' I said soothingly. The panacea for all ills – Eric loved tea.

I squeezed the sack of hay into a dark part of the passage beyond my wardrobe out there and the sickle – used by me for cutting any long grass suitable for hay – went under *my* bed, this time.

Later that morning I was called out to rescue three young starlings that had fallen down a chimney. This happened fairly frequently; starlings and sparrows seemed to make a habit of it in the spring. For nearly twenty minutes I lay flat on my stomach on a young chap's hearthrug with both arms round a gas-fire, reaching into the chimney cavity. I was trying to grasp the three frightened fledglings crouching there, but even with the young fellow's help – he was on the floor too – it was very difficult; always they cowered away in the dark, sooty depths away from our fingers. We could hear them but couldn't see them because of the fire. Eventually we succeeded.

The weakest fledgling died, but I was able to rear the other two successfully and eventually release them.

Many people think starlings greedy quarrelsome birds, but I like them. Like sparrows, they are opportunists, but they do a lot of good in the garden and are intelligent, cheerful and bright as buttons, I find.

One day about a week later I was handed an adult starling that had been found on the motorway by a young couple I knew.

'It was twisting and fluttering on its back and being blown about like a piece of black paper on the road,' Carol said. 'Alan didn't want to stop but I made him. Poor thing, we couldn't just drive on and leave it, could we?'

Stanley, as I called him, was suffering pretty badly from shock as well as concussion, not surprisingly, and I kept him very quiet in a box for several days. He recovered, but, although his wings appeared undamaged and his legs weren't broken, I noticed he couldn't stand nor even remain upright unless propped. There seemed to be something wrong with his back, causing paralysis of the legs. I hoped it would only be temporary; the vet said nothing could be done about it.

He was alert and quite cheerful, however, and had a good appetite, so I hoped in time he'd regain the use of his legs.

I forget exactly how it started but I got into the habit of taking Stanley insect-hunting in the garden, starlings being avid insect eaters. I used to hold him in one hand rather as you'd hold a small hoover, beak downwards, while he gobbled up all the many insects hiding under the stones in the rockery. Gripping him firmly but gently round his middle, I turned over each rock with my other hand and Stanley dived forwards with outstretched neck, eating everything in sight. There were many insects to be found and he had a great time gulping down woodlice, worms, slugs, millepedes, centipedes, beetles and the occasional grub. Ants he declined; a pity, as we had many: black ones, red ones . . . you name them, we had them in our rockery, all scurrying around moving their eggs away from the monster lifting the stones.

On the rare occasions when there was nothing to be seen under a rock the starling stabbed his sharp pointed beak into the earth, opened it, withdrew, then prodded back into the conical hole he'd made and invariably came up with a juicy worm or some other tit-bit that hadn't even been visible. This, of course, was a starling's normal procedure and what you see them doing on the lawn. I used to marvel at the way he always came up with something; how did he know anything was down there?

I took Stanley insect-hunting like this about twice a day, or whenever I had time. He loved it. He always lay motionless in my hand, never attempting to struggle and sometimes nearly fell from my fingers in his eagerness to perform his duty as pest-controller as we approached a rock, his bright little eyes never missing a thing. Never had our large, sprawling rockery been so insect-free! After a few weeks I had to search elsewhere, and I used to roam the garden and fields all around hunting for insects, the mini 'hoover' in my hand, beak down at the ready. There he'd lie, still and expectant, as I walked round bending and turning stones over.

Alas, poor Stanley, his legs didn't improve but appeared to be permanently paralysed; something to do with the central nervous system, it was thought. When he wasn't out foraging with me I had him propped up as comfortably as possible in a cardboard-box with a mirror for company, but if he attempted to move he fell over.

One day in the garden I'd been feeding Stanley worms in his box while weeding the border. He loved the sun on his back, as most birds do, and I took him outside whenever I could. Worms were his favourite food. On this occasion he'd already eaten quite a few when I gave him an extra large one, thinking he'd break it up as he usually did before swallowing it. He gave a series of large gulps at the whole worm, however, and it seemed to go down although the creature was still visible in his open beak and it had seemed a bit of a struggle.

I had to go out for half an hour then, so I carried the starling and box indoors and left him to it, still gulping his reluctant worm. He seemed quite happy; the worm was putting up a fight but I thought Stanley was winning.

But when I got back poor Stanley was dead. I found him lying on his side, part of that last worm still sticking out of his open beak, his head in the corner of the box. It is my belief he choked to death possibly by falling over as the large worm still endeavoured to escape, the way he fell restricting his air passage.

I was very upset, of course, and blamed myself for leaving him . . .

and for giving him so large a worm. Yet, I thought, perhaps it was for the best? It looked as if he'd always have been a hopeless cripple, and unlike my little thrush, Tom, I didn't think Stanley was the sort of bird to be content just sitting around watching things all day long; he wasn't tame enough. So perhaps the little starling would rather have died as he did in this way – eating his favourite food?

=23=

PHEASANT
ON THE COMPUTER

I HAD divided one of the large wooden cages into two, which proved very useful. I found an unused Daler board – left over from my painting days – which fitted almost perfectly across the centre of the cage in a horizontal position, making each half about a foot in height and acting as a floor for what was to be known as the Top Flat and ceiling for the Lower Flat. I fixed it in position with strong paper clips and wooden struts. Then I had to divide the door into two parts so that each 'flat' could be opened separately. I was very pleased with this arrangement and of course I could always remove the board at any time and have one large cage again. Which I sometimes did.

Late one evening the phone rang and a man living on a housing estate about five miles away asked if I could come and collect a tawny owl.

'It's been hit by a car,' he said. 'We've carried it into the kitchen.'

'Can you bring it to me here?' I asked hopefully. It was nearly ten o'clock and I was tired after a hectic day. Eric had just finished a late supper and was watching television prior to going to bed early. Besides, petrol was expensive.

'No . . . we haven't any transport. I'm afraid not.'

I sighed. 'All right, then. I'll be round in about twenty minutes.'

'What was it?' Eric asked when I got back from the phone.

I hardly dared tell him – I thought he'd be mad at someone expecting me to go out at this time of night.

'Er . . . someone's found an owl. It's been hit by a car, apparently. He wants it fetched.'

'Where?'

I named the place expecting him to sit up and yell 'What?' but

123

instead he said, 'I'll drive you there.' Adding, 'You'll only get lost if you try and find it on your own.'

He was right, of course. I didn't know the area at all and it was never easy finding one specific house on a housing estate in the dark. It took us some time to find the right house; the estate was large and it was very difficult to see the numbers at night – I was glad Eric was with me. As it was I had to keep getting out and shining the torch. There were few lights anywhere.

The tawny owl was in a box on the kitchen floor, covered with a large blanket.

'It's quite fierce,' said the man as he and his family crowded round.

'Yes, goes for you, it does,' added his wife, standing well back as I bent to uncover the box.

Gingerly I lifted the blanket. The tawny owl blinked at the sudden bright light, crouching low in the box. It was larger than Wol and I decided it was probably an adult female. Gently I lifted her into the box I'd brought, covering it with a cloth. She didn't seem very fierce to me. As we drove home I wondered vaguely what an owl was doing in the centre of a housing estate with scarcely a field or tree in sight; it seemed odd.

Olive, as I called her, was suffering from concussion but was otherwise unhurt. She remained motionless in a comfortable box for several days. Now and then I opened her beak and popped in a small piece of ox heart which she obligingly swallowed, but it was eight days before she moved or appeared aware of what was going on and two weeks before she could perch and act more normally.

Wol, needless to say, was very interested in the new owl, alighting on her box on several occasions and peering inside, head rotating wildly. The only time they met in the room, however, when Olive unexpectedly jumped out of her box, he tried to attack her, puffing himself out to look fierce and all set to chase the intruder away in a most ungallant fashion.

'Look out!' Eric shouted – I had gone into his room for something – 'There's going to be a fight.'

'A what?' I hadn't heard properly.

'Wol and Olive . . . you'd better come quickly and see.'

I hurried back into the room and put Olive back in her box and Wol in his cage. I didn't think an owl fight was a good thing at all.

We took Olive to a lady living some miles away who specialized in owls and the rehabilitating of these beautiful birds, and she put her in an outside aviary to recuperate. When fully recovered she was released in the woods bordering the lady's large garden and flew happily away. There were owl nesting-boxes, feeding posts and plenty of other owls around for company. Olive would be fine.

A few days later a girl brought round a tiny pheasant chick for me to rear.

'Ah, isn't it sweet?' I enthused, never having seen one close to before. 'Where did you find it?'

Her answer certainly surprised me.

'On top of a computer – in the office where I work,' she said. 'I know it sounds peculiar, but that's where it was.'

She explained that she worked in a private house, taken over by her firm and near some farmland.

'But how on earth did it get there?'

'Honestly . . . we don't know. All we can think of is that our golden retriever dog must have found it and brought it indoors. Someone must have picked it up and placed it on the computer.'

The pheasant chick was a pretty little thing, biscuit coloured with dark stripes down his back. He couldn't have been more than one, maybe two, days old. I named him Tigger.

For two days the chick refused to eat properly and I was worried as to whether he was going to survive. He turned down everything I offered including soaked chick crumbs, biscuit, hard-boiled egg yolk, bread-and-milk, Farex and seed, and when forcibly fed he did his best to spit it out, seeming very unhappy. I rang up a friend who I knew had reared pheasant chicks; this was my first.

'You do realize they eat a lot of meat, don't you?' he said. 'Worms and things. The mother bird feeds them these in the wild.'

'No,' I answered. 'I hadn't realized that.' I felt ashamed of my ignorance. Raw meat was about the only thing I *hadn't* tried on Tigger. I tried him with some . . . and he gobbled it up straight away.

After about a week of raw mince diet the little chick started eating canary seed and crumbs, also picking up tiny insects from the soil in his box. After two weeks I took him into the garden and placed him under the large Twilweld cloche I used for birds sometimes. I was surprised at the way the pheasant chick pulled up small worms and slugs and found insects in the turf which he ate with great gusto; I hadn't believed that such an innocent looking piece of lawn could harbour such a hoard of creatures, none of which had been visible to *me*.

Tigger had tiny wing feathers growing now and his legs were longer. I learned that game birds develop wing feathers and learn to fly very quickly – the exact opposite of water-fowl whose wings usually develop last of all.

I made the Top Flat of the divided cage into a sort of indoor garden for Tigger and during the day he pecked around up there, at night preferring his cosy box. The Lower Flat was occupied by three little sparrows; one called Twinky was very tame and flew in and out of the cage when I opened a small flap I'd cut in the wire. She was one I'd reared and she couldn't fly well enough for release but she enjoyed an occasional sortie out into the room.

After four weeks Tigger was fully fledged and able to fly; he was about half the size of an adult pheasant. He was very tame and liked perching on my knee, lying by the fire or exploring the room. Like Wol he loved the small bowl fire on chilly days. He used to lie very close with his long legs outstretched, toasting first one side and then the other, his wings fanned out.

'That pheasant,' announced Eric' one evening, putting down his paper and glaring at the prone Tigger, 'that pheasant is taking up all the fire. I can't get my legs anywhere near it.'

I turned from the wash-basin. 'Tigger . . . come on, move over!' He got up slowly and reluctantly and stalked away rather huffily.

His stripes had almost disappeared now, having been replaced with pretty mottled-brown colouring; his legs were silvery blue-grey, and he resembled a young turkey in shape. When he was eleven weeks old Tigger went to live in Pam's aviary for a time. He was a handsome cock pheasant now with a red face and long tail feathers growing. Since he was still very tame I was told it would be unsafe to release him in the wild, as I'd intended, as tame pheasants were inclined to hang around and get themselves shot. And he'd become too large for me to continue keeping indoors.

Some weeks later Tigger was found a nice home with a gentleman who bred silver and gold pheasants. He was put in a special enclosure of his own but where he could see the others . . . and was promised a hen pheasant for company.

=24=

THE DUCK AND
THE CROW

'I SEE there's a duck in my room,' announced Eric one evening. His voice was reasonably calm; he'd got used to this sort of thing.

'Yes. That's Lucy.'

'What's up with her?'

I explained how I'd rescued her that afternoon when she'd been found crouching against the wall of a block of flats near the river.

'She was in an awful state,' I told him. 'Water-logged and shivering, with a lump in her throat, her crop split open and a little crippled leg. She made no attempt to fly away at all when I approached but just lay there and let me pick her up, poor little thing.'

'Hmm. I see.' He peered into the large rectangular box on the trunk in his room where Lucy crouched in the hay. 'Well, I hope she won't make a noise in the night.'

'I don't think so . . . she's scarcely moved. I took her to the vet and he's stitched up her crop. But he can't do anything about her leg, of course.'

Lucy's leg was twisted and the foot screwed up close to her body, making her virtually one-legged. She had to hop everywhere. The vet thought she had either been born with the little deformed leg or else it had been broken, perhaps when she was a duckling, and had set like that. It wasn't a recent injury.

The little brown duck – she looked like a mallard-cross, being lighter brown in colour without the speculum – had stopped shivering now, thanks to a hot-water bottle each side of her, and was eating some bread-and-milk. She wouldn't touch chick crumbs. The lump in her throat seemed to have gone, whatever it was, but it might be some time before her feathers became waterproof again. She was extremely

127

nervous, frightened even of the water and food bowls I placed in her box and when touched she trembled with fright. I believed she must have been lightly struck by a boat on the river.

Lucy was quiet in the night and Eric agreed that she could stay in his room, which was a relief as I'd really nowhere else to put her. He got quite fond of her, actually, and used to chat to her occasionally. Gradually over the weeks the little duck got used to us and became less nervous, quite enjoying it when I sat her on my knee and stroked her head feathers and fondled her neck, a thing ducks seemed to like, I'd discovered. Soon she was quite at home in my room when I let her out of the box, hopping around on her good leg and often settling under the armchair for a nap.

One day Lucy decided to hop across the room to the empty sparrow cage under my north window. I had left this cage empty and placed just one broad single perch inside because my crow, Crusoe, had recently taken to jumping out of his cage on the chest-of-drawers near the door every afternoon and taking his siesta in there.

Now Crusoe was a real character – a funny old crow with a mind of his own and a nasty temper at times. He'd originally been brought by some people who were worried about the fact that he'd been hanging around their garden for a week and not flown away. They'd thrown him bread and even brought him into their kitchen at night, putting him outside on the lawn each morning. 'But he never seems to fly away,' the lady told me on the phone. 'We don't know why. We've called him Crusoe.' They hadn't realized his wing was broken; it was an old injury, the vet said; the wing was locked and he couldn't move it.

So Crusoe came to live with us and quickly made himself at home.

'What's that black thing up there?' Eric had asked rather insultingly when he first saw the crow.

'A crow,' I'd answered. 'He's called Crusoe.'

Then the usual question: 'What's up with him?'

Eric got up from the table that day and said hello to the 'new boy', holding out a finger to scratch Crusoe's head. Crusoe promptly pecked it, drawing blood.

'You little b . . . . r!' my husband exclaimed, retreating hurriedly and sucking the finger. 'I don't like *him*!'

Not a good beginning.

Crusoe didn't think much of any of the other resident birds, nor did he like any other member of the crow family I'd ever had. He had arthriticky legs which had responded well to Cortizone tablets, but it had left him with a peculiar 'gammy-leg' gait when he walked. His cage with the drop-front was always open and he took a great interest in all that was going on, accepting tit-bits of almost anything from chocolate to cheese – his two favourite things, together with egg. Sometimes I paused when passing to massage his neck or ruffle his head feathers, which put him in a state of ecstasy. He could be really soppy at times and go into a sort of trance when you did his neck as he lowered his head until his beak almost touched his toes, eyes closed, but he wasn't beyond jerking up and giving the soothing fingers a sharp blood-drawing peck if the mood took him. I think, like Jacko, he just did this for the hell of it and not because he was really vicious; he usually had the same wicked twinkle in his eye. He had large, very expressive eyes – 'like a spaniel', Eric said – and would blink rapidly when pleased.

We'd grown very fond of Crusoe.

So there was Lucy making her way to the empty sparrow cage – the crow's favourite place for an afternoon nap – and I just knew there was going to be trouble . . .

Lucy reached the cage, liked the look of it – and decided to stay. Settling herself comfortably in the shadows at the back she put her head under her wing and went to sleep. It was nice and dark in there and just the place for a snooze.

Oh dear.

Crusoe hadn't seen her go in there as he'd been busy poking around in the back of his cage for a bit of hidden cheese – crows hide food constantly – and at around two fifteen, his usual time, he sprang out of the cage and walked gammily across the room and straight into the sparrow cage. I watched with bated breath. Lucy looked up, stretched out her neck defensively and hissed a warning: Keep away! Crusoe turned and fled back across the room as if all the bats in hell were after him, wanting to be lifted back into his cage again and grumbling away to himself in the way that crows do. It took me about ten minutes to comfort the poor chap – he was literally trembling – and he was very put out indeed, I could tell. A duck in my siesta cage? The very idea!

The following afternoon the same thing happened; Lucy had decided it was now *her* siesta cage! – and every day that week there was trouble, both birds being equally determined they were going to take possession of that sparrow cage under the window. There was never actually a fight or anything, but much ill-feeling on Crusoe's part. Sometimes the crow got there first, only to jump off the perch and flee at Lucy's approach, bounding with leaps across the room and grumbling away like anything.

The feud continued, but Lucy won in the end, holding her ground. Crusoe stopped jumping out of his cage and took his afternoon nap perched up there on the chest-of-drawers. Peace reigned again . . . But he remained scared stiff of my meek little brown duck. He wasn't very brave . . . or gallant.

My funny old crow not only 'grumbled' but had a vocabulary of many weird and wonderful noises which he produced at times. Some of them could be likened to a cough, a dog barking, heavy panting (this with beak pointed upwards and eyes blinking rapidly), a kind of howl, and loud maniacal laughter and cackling. Most of these noises were very loud, when he got going, and we used to yell, 'Crusoe . . . shut *up*!' or '*Do* be quiet!' for fear he'd disturb the other tenants. There was a bathroom and toilet next to my room and I'm certain that sometimes new tenants walking past my door must have gone away shaking their heads and muttering, 'That poor, demented lady in there . . . obviously she's quite nutty.' Crusoe's maniacal cackling sounded far more like an old witch than anything a mere crow could produce and not everyone knew I had birds. 'I could hear that bloody crow right across the hall!' announced Eric one day as he entered the room and stabbed a finger in the general direction of Crusoe. 'Cover him up.'

I was worried about whether I should release Lucy or not. Obviously she was very handicapped, even swimming, with only one usable leg, and I wasn't sure if she'd survive in the wild. The picture of that shivering, soaked and miserable little duck crouching against the brick building was still fresh in my mind; I didn't want to risk that ever happening to her again. I wrote to the Wildfowl Trust explaining all about Lucy and asking their advice. They wrote back recommending that I kept her, adding that getting her a mate for company would be a nice idea. So Lucy stayed and joined my little band of 'residents'.

Every day Lucy bathed in a bowl of water. She had grown much tamer now, and when the weather grew warmer I started carrying her across the field to the lake about twice a week in my nylon shopping bag for a swim. There was a shallow rocky pool where a stream emerged from underground and fed into the lake and Lucy had a great time splashing about and swimming in this pool; when I took her there for the first time she was as excited as a small child seeing the sea for the first time and I thought I'd never persuade her to come out. But normally after about twenty minutes she was quite ready to come home and preen and dry herself back in my room. She lay quite still in the nylon carrier-bag while I was carrying her, each way.

One day Lucy was to get her mate. But that was in the future.

= 25 =

LITTLE BIRDS
AND SMALL ANIMALS

I WAS sorry that the tall elms all round the garden and field had gone. Slowly they had died of Dutch elm disease, some thirty of them, the leaves shrivelling and trunks peeling, and now they had been felled, too dangerous to leave standing. It had completely changed the old familiar landscapes. I especially missed the elm opposite my side window; there was a branch that used to wave friendly green leaves at me only a few feet away throughout the summer and it was a favourite haunt of nuthatches, even more so when it died and was full of insects.

The nuthatches had been coming to my window sill for peanuts for several years. Cheerful, compact, pretty little pink and slate-blue birds: I loved watching them. We used to see them creeping down the trunk in search of insects, twisting round and round the tree as they descended head-first. Tree-creepers were less frequent visitors, and I was once very amused to see a nuthatch working its way down the tree and almost bump into a tree-creeper working up the same trunk. I noticed the former usually worked downwards and the latter upwards, though I don't know whether this is the general rule.

But now the trees had gone and I never saw my friendly little nuthatches again, though they could be heard across in the lake woods still. I think they nested on one of the tiny islands there.

One day Eric brought home a baby bullfinch found fallen from a tree, I was told, and handed to him in the garage. He was a handsome, friendly little chap and as tame as a budgie – I called him Bully.

Soon the little bullfinch was flying round the room making his rather plaintive call, often alighting on my head or shoulders. He was a seed-eater, of course, but too young to eat packet seed yet – there was something called British Finch Mixture that I used to buy for adult finches – so I used to go into the fields and shake the seeding heads of the tall grasses so they released the seed into a large paper bag, mixing these with moistened stale brown bread and some Bemax and making small 'rissoles' which I fed to Bully with a pair of scissor-type eyebrow tweezers I kept for this purpose. He loved them and seemed to do very well on this diet, eventually learning to pick up the 'rissoles' for himself.

After three weeks I was able to release him in the garden. He had grown into a fine young bird, and I often saw him around in the old fruit trees. Later he was joined by other bullfinch youngsters.

Olly was another friendly little finch who was brought shortly afterwards by an attractive Scottish girl carrying an eighteen-month-old baby. He was a greenfinch fledgling found fallen from a nest in their garden; he was a charming little fellow, so tame that he perched on the baby's chubby finger without fear as she smiled and gurgled with delight, starting to cry at having to leave the little bird as she was carried away. They had had Olly two weeks but now wanted me to take him as they were going away for a few days.

I had a sparrow I was rearing that was about the same age and the two little birds shared a cage and soon became firm friends, eating from the same dish, perching side by side at night, and flying, hopping and twittering round the room together during the day.

Olly was with me five weeks before flying from the window to join a small flock of greenfinches in the garden. I had seen them in the field and had been waiting until they came nearer before releasing him. The week before he went the girl and baby came to say goodbye to him, but the greenfinch flew up on to the high perch and refused to come down. They hardly recognized him and he didn't seem to know them any more. Though we were all rather disappointed at his unfriendliness, he was a fine young adult now; the girl was pleased to see him looking so well.

During the winter that followed a solitary male greenfinch, resplendent in bright new green and yellow plumage, came and alighted outside on my window sill to feed. I felt sure it was Olly. There were other greenfinches chattering in the bushes but only the one was brave enough to come to the window. Nor had any other greenfinch ever been to the sill before, to my knowledge.

The sparrow, Cheeky, flew away too and joined other sparrows in the old plum-tree at the side of the lawn, where they squabbled and twittered in a noisy flock most afternoons.

I had two other interesting little birds that summer: swallow fledglings. I'd never had a swallow before, though house-martins were brought fairly frequently. Both species were difficult to rear because of the feeding; one had to find a satisfactory substitute for the thousands of tiny flies they'd normally consume each day. One of the fledglings died after four days, but the other one seemed to be doing well and I was very pleased with him. I called him Sam.

Sam became very tame, perching unafraid on any finger held out to him and flitting about the room. He loved to perch on the kettle, and was a most happy little chap. Every morning he had a bath in a shallow dish of water placed on the table, fluttering and splashing about for several minutes. He had very short little feathered legs and wings that had not yet developed into the slender, tapered wings of an adult swallow, crossing over the back. I fed him on any small flies I could find and tiny bits of raw mince, together with some of the special mixture I made for swifts.

I had great hopes of eventually releasing the little swallow to join the others on their long migratory flight to Africa that autumn, but alas, it was not to be. Eric and I had arranged to go away for three days – it was the only holiday we had that year – and Pam kindly offered to look after Sam, Crusoe, Lucy and the other birds. Wol and Stikki were going to another friend.

The very morning we left Sam seemed a little off colour and hadn't eaten well that morning. I was worried about leaving him as we stopped at Pam's on the way and dropped off the birds she was having.

'Don't worry . . . he'll be all right,' Pam reassured me in her usual cheerful way. 'Have a nice time!'

'Stop worrying!' said Eric much later, as I wondered if Sam was all right for the umpteenth time while we were away. 'He'll be all right.' But for some reason I *was* worried . . . all the time.

We stopped for a meal the evening we drove home and I rang Pam. No reply. I didn't really enjoy that dinner. An hour later we stopped at her house and I hurried to the door. Sam was dead. The other birds were fine.

Whether it was the change or very hot weather that had upset the little swallow we never knew but apparently he went off his food and died just before we returned. I was very sad and disappointed, but I knew my friend had done her best for him. These things happen sometimes.

One day a young fellow rang up from one of the local boat-yards.

'We've found a kestrel . . . it was on the road. Could you call round and collect it, please?'

I said I would and found a fairly large box, wondering what a kestrel was doing in that unlikely area.

A boy clattered down the wooden stairs holding something cupped in his hands when I arrived at the yard. He must have also found an injured sparrow or something, I thought – there were many around.

He opened his fingers cautiously. 'Here it is . . . the kestrel.'

I stared at the small dark brown bird and he saw the look in my eye. '*Isn't* it?'

'Well, no. It's a young swift, actually.'

'There y'are!' his mate jeered. 'I told you! I know my birds, I do.'

Happily the swift was only suffering from slight concussion; it recovered and was released a few days later.

Occasionally I was brought small animals: hedgehogs, squirrels, bats and once a baby weasel. Sadly the latter died after three days. It was a tiny, blind little creature and extremely difficult to feed.

One lady I knew was having trouble with bats in her attic. The first one she brought me was a baby; it was smaller than a postage stamp and I had to get a magnifying glass in order to see which end to feed, I remember! The second gave me a nasty shock, climbing out of its box in the night and appearing like a small square black patch under the shade of my bedside lamp, the squeaking noise it made waking me.

The following night was worse; in the wee small hours I was again woken by tiny squeaks. Putting on my light I found the little thing apparently planning to get into bed with me; it was clinging to the top sheet right in front of my chin as I lay on my back. It gave me a real fright and once again I was thankful we hadn't been watching a late-night Dracula film.

On both occasions it was a complete mystery as to how the little bat escaped from what I thought was a completely escape-proof box.

The squirrels came late summer.

'What have you got there?' I asked the man extracting a large box from the boot of his car. I hoped it wasn't anything large, like a crow or seagull. I just hadn't the room.

'Three baby squirrels,' his wife replied, smiling at me. 'You, er, do take animals, don't you?' She asked anxiously. 'Only we found them at the foot of a tree – must have fallen from a nest.'

'I know they're supposed to be vermin,' the man said as he carried the box indoors. 'But . . . well, we couldn't leave them to die, could we?'

'No, of course not,' I smiled, 'I'll certainly take them.'

After they'd gone there was a moment of slight panic: three *squirrels*?

They'd wreck the place, wouldn't they, when they got bigger? Eric would go *mad*! Where could I *put* them?

I made the three squirming babies comfortable in a box and then fed them warm milk with a small pipette. They drank greedily, then curled up for a snooze in the warm bed of hay. The old Tin Lizzie hot-water bottle was there, too, encased in what I sincerely hoped was one of Eric's discarded woolly socks.

Eric didn't go mad but he had grave misgivings and was far from delighted. '*Squirrels*? What are you going to do when they grow big? Don't ever let them out in the room or they'll wreck the place! It's bad enough with the birds.'

The three little grey squirrels were with me five weeks and they grew from helpless babies to perfect little mini bushy-tailed squirrels in that time. When they were small I found it better to feed them with a plastic syringe with a piece of valve rubber over the nozzle, and they gripped this with tiny paws as they sucked the milk. They loved milk, taking it from a drip-feeder when they grew older and were installed in one of the wooden cages. Between them they consumed about three quarters of a pint daily, as well as nuts, berries and biscuits when they grew large and became very active. I daren't let them out into the room but they had a great time playing 'chase me' round the cage, leaping on and off the tree branches and chasing each other round and round. I called them Sally, Susie and Sammy. They seemed perfectly happy in the cage, never attempting to jump out when I opened the door. They were dear little things and, rather suprisingly, most well behaved.

When they were old enough and I was sure able to fend for themselves I carried them in a box to the lake woods. For some minutes nothing happened when I opened the lid, then first one and then the other two timidly ventured out. Then each squirrel scampered up a different tree – also surprising – quickly disappearing in the foliage. There were plenty of other squirrels about, so they'd have company. And for several days I took nuts and biscuits there and laid them in a little pile at the foot of a tree.

'*Squirrels*' said my farmer's wife sister when I told her about them later. '*Grey* squirrels? You should have killed them.' She glared at me sternly.

I had strong views on this subject. They were charming little animals, vermin or not, and I felt as I always do about such things, namely that they didn't ask to be born and having been brought into the world they were entitled to live their lives just like any other creature. Man, I've always felt, is often a little too fond of decreeing what shall live and what shall die. Usually to further his own ends.

Gloria Gobbledegook came about the same time. She was a young coot. She'd been found strolling down the middle of a road, obviously lost, and was such a funny little thing that I thought she should have a funny name; with their rust-coloured wiry hair on their necks – the texture of a door-mat – and little red beaks with snowy white tips and floppy lobed feet, coot chicks always amused me.

She was most awkward to feed, refusing most things. Then she decided she liked soaked Go Cat, but not bread-and-milk, and ate this nicely for three days. On the fourth day, however, she decided she only liked bread-and-milk and wouldn't touch the Go Cat. Fair enough. But on the fifth day 'Gooky' wouldn't touch either, refusing both Go Cat and bread-and-milk. She decided to eat only raw mince and green stuff . . . both refused on the first four days!

Gooky was with me six weeks, developing in the same way as Topsy. She, too, became very tame and cuddly, but unlike the moorhen refused to use a Polythene 'lavatory' – coots won't – so had to be confined to a pen indoors. She grew very friendly with Lucy, the latter graciously allowing her into the sparrow cage for a snooze with her some afternoons.

Eventually Gloria Gobbledegook was released on the lake. There were plenty of other coots there and she swam away quite happily.

=26=

ANOTHER YEAR OVER

ANOTHER year over with the usual trickle of birds coming in during the winter, and now spring and the 'busy season' just around the corner. Blackbirds are lingering purposefully near their favourite nesting places, sparrows are gathering under the eaves and the starlings have already started building in the same jutting-out piece of drainpipe that they nest in year in year out.

In the last four years I've tended nearly six hundred wild birds. Single-handed and in this small room it's been hard and demanding work, especially with the endless problems that crop up in the confined space and without any aviaries. But it's been infinitely worthwhile. It's also been fascinating, rewarding and utterly absorbing. In these modern times sentiment seems to be a dirty word. This saddens me, always, as I firmly believe that the world would be a much better place with much *more* sentiment and affection dished out to animals and humans alike. I therefore make no apologies for admitting freely and unashamedly that I've showered affection on all my birds whenever possible, caressing and cuddling them to show the love that was in my heart. And before anyone says 'Yuk!', let me tell you they love it! They've responded by returning my affection in their own way, frightened birds quietening, sick birds recovering and baby birds thriving. I've loved them all, grieving for the ones that inevitably died and rejoicing for those that recovered to fly away, much as I missed them. Miss them I always did, because they became my friends as well as my patients.

I've heard it said that a tame 'humanized' bird won't survive in the wild, but I've never found this to be the case. Often I've met up with birds I've released weeks or months later and they all seemed to be doing just fine. One moorhen I reared returned to see me several times at six-monthly intervals, allowing me to touch her but not to handle her, and some have returned with their mates or young. And as already explained, many birds become 'wild' again when adult or fully fit, settling very quickly in their natural habitat.

It's always sad when a bird dies, especially when it's one you've tried desperately to save or have tenderly nursed for a long time. But as my friend Pam always says, 'Well, at least it died knowing someone cared.'

I'm sure the mother starling realized this when she was brought to me, dying, in a box with her naked, blind baby beside her. She had a fish-hook lodged deep in her throat and had been found early morning tangled up in the ivy by the nylon fishing-line attached, close to her nest near a house. The other babies were dead, but the schoolboy who found them brought me the survivor, cold and almost dead, along with the mother bird.

I put them both in a warm box and fed and cared for the baby starling, managing to save its life. I like to think the mother bird died, as she did half an hour later, knowing her young one was in good hands and would live.

The young starling grew into a fine, healthy adult and stayed around several months before flying off to join a flock of starlings in the garden. His mum would have been proud of him.

Very soon now we will be moving to a small pre-fab bungalow in the grounds of the old house. It has four rooms and a small garden, and already I am planning a little duck-pen for Lucy in the corner of the latter, and a pool for her to swim in. I'm sure she will be pleased. But now I see that Wol is standing in his green bath a few feet away, his talons making little scratchy noises as he fidgets, waiting.

I must go and get a jug of water . . .